The History of the U.S. Army Corps of Engineers

Office of History
Headquarters, U.S. Army Corps of Engineers

University Press of the Pacific
Honolulu, Hawaii

The History of the U.S. Army Corps of Engineers

by
Office of History
U.S. Army Corps of Engineers

ISBN: 1-4102-1059-6

Reprinted from the 1998 edition

University Press of the Pacific
Honolulu, Hawaii
http://www.universitypressofthepacific.com

Foreword

This short, illustrated history of the U.S. Army Corps of Engineers provides an overview of the many missions that engineers have performed in support of the Army and the nation since the early days of the American Revolution. A permanent institution since 1802, the U.S. Army Corps of Engineers has effectively and proudly responded to changing defense requirements and has played an integral part in the development of the nation.

Engineers have served in combat in all our nation's wars. Throughout the 19th century the Corps built coastal fortifications, surveyed roads and canals, eliminated navigational hazards, explored and mapped the western frontier, and constructed buildings and monuments in the nation's capital.

In the 20th century, the Corps became the lead federal flood control agency. Assigned the military construction mission in 1941, the Corps constructed facilities at home and abroad to support the Army and the Air Force. During the Cold War, Army engineers managed construction programs for America's allies, including a massive effort in Saudi Arabia.

Today, building on its rich heritage, the Corps is changing to meet the challenges of tomorrow. Our vision calls for us to be a vital part of the Army; the engineer team of choice, responding to our nation's needs in peace and war; and a values-based organization, respected, responsive, and reliable.

I hope that readers of this history will gain an appreciation of the military, political, economic, and technological factors that shaped the modern Corps of Engineers. We in the Corps, both soldiers and civilians, are proud of our many contributions to the Army and the nation and look forward with confidence to continued service.

JOE N. BALLARD
Lieutenant General, USA
Commanding

Office of History
Headquarters, U.S. Army Corps of Engineers

The History of the U.S. Army Corps of Engineers

Contents

1 Foreword

2 Historical Time Line

17 The Revolutionary War

21 Union with the Artillerists

23 Engineers in the War of 1812

25 The Corps and the Military Academy at West Point, 1802–1866

29 Explorations and Surveys

33 The National Road

35 Lighthouses

37 Origins of Civil Works Missions

41 Waterway Development

47 Flood Control

53 Hydropower Development

57 The Environmental Challenge

61 Work in the District of Columbia

65 Coast Defense

69 Combat Operations from the Mexican War to the Mexican Punitive Expedition

75 The Panama Canal

79 U.S. Army Engineers in World War I

83 Combat Engineers in World War II

91 The Manhattan Project

95 Engineer Combat in Korea and Vietnam

101 Military Construction

105 The Corps and the Space Program

109 Work for Other Nations

115 Changing Military Responsibilities and Relationships

127 Civil Works, Congress, and the Executive Branch

138 The Corps Castle and Essayons Button

139 Portraits and Profiles

153 Selected Bibliography

CORPS OF ENGINEERS HISTORICAL TIME LINE

1775

Congress established Continental Army with provision for a Chief Engineer (June 16). Richard Gridley named first Chief Engineer and oversaw fortification at the Battle of Bunker Hill.

1779

Engineer officers and companies of sappers and miners formed into a Corps of Engineers.

1781

French and American engineer officers and sappers and miners played key role in successful Siege of Yorktown.

1783

Corps of Engineers mustered out of service along with most of the Continental Army.

1794

Unified Corps of Artillerists and Engineers established.

Col. William Prescott at the Battle of Bunker Hill, painting by Frederick C. Yohn.

The Continental Insurance Compa

Battle of Bunker Hill. 1878 lithograph

Library of Congress

Plan of attack for Yorktown, drawn by Jean Baptiste de Gouvion, October 29, 1781.

National Archives

2

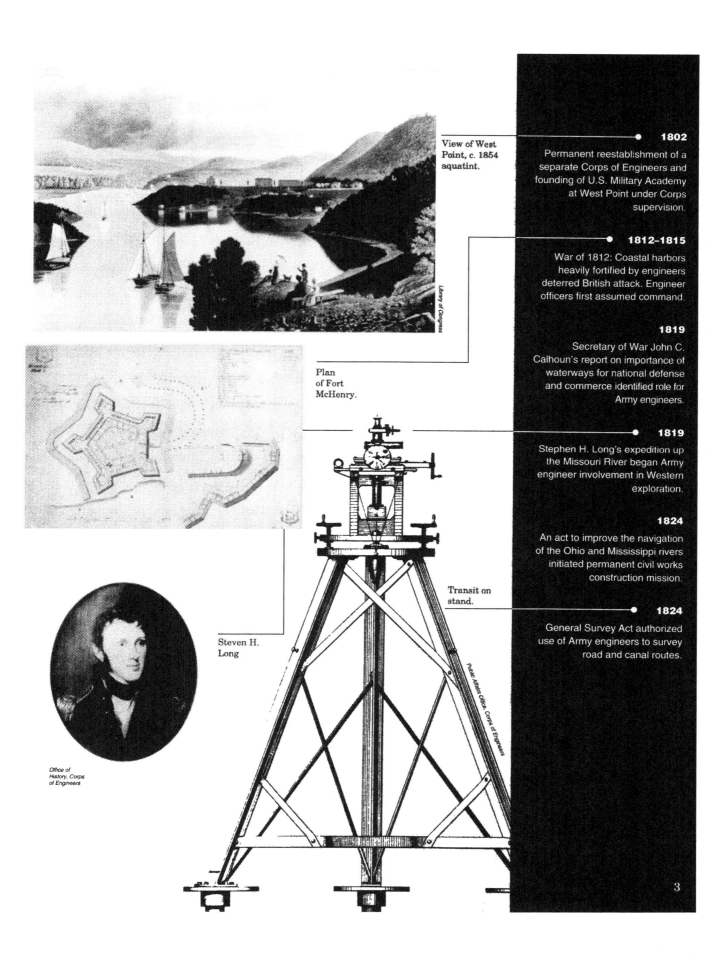

View of West
Point, c. 1854
aquatint.

Library of Congress

Plan
of Fort
McHenry.

Steven H.
Long

*Office of
History, Corps
of Engineers*

Transit on
stand.

Public Affairs Office, Corps of Engineers

1802

Permanent reestablishment of a
separate Corps of Engineers and
founding of U.S. Military Academy
at West Point under Corps
supervision.

1812–1815

War of 1812: Coastal harbors
heavily fortified by engineers
deterred British attack. Engineer
officers first assumed command.

1819

Secretary of War John C.
Calhoun's report on importance of
waterways for national defense
and commerce identified role for
Army engineers.

1819

Stephen H. Long's expedition up
the Missouri River began Army
engineer involvement in Western
exploration.

1824

An act to improve the navigation
of the Ohio and Mississippi rivers
initiated permanent civil works
construction mission.

1824

General Survey Act authorized
use of Army engineers to survey
road and canal routes.

1825

Corps assumed responsibility for construction and repair of Cumberland Road.

1829

Corps launched first steam-powered snagboat *Helepolis* on the Mississippi River.

1838

Creation of separate Corps of Topographical Engineers under Colonel John J. Abert.

1840s

Fremont's expeditions to Rockies and beyond provided vital information on lands, peoples, and resources of the West.

1846

Creation of first company of regular Army engineer troops.

1846–1848

Mexican War: Engineer regulars erected fortifications and joined in assaults. Officers performed key reconnaissance missions.

1853

District of Columbia water supply work commenced as forerunner of Corps' Washington Aqueduct Office.

4

Shreve's snag-boat *Helepolis*

1893 stamp depicting John C. Fremont's ascent of Snow Peak.

Siege of Vera Cruz, 1847.

Influent gate house, Georgetown Reservoir, December 1858.

Joining of Central Pacific and Union Pacific railroads at Promontory Point, Utah.

Public Affairs Office, Corps of Engineers

Gouverneur K. Warren, as a cadet.

U.S. Military Academy Library

Company A, U.S. Engineers, 1865.

Office of History, Corps of Engineers

Senate wing and Capitol dome under construction, 1863.

Office of History, Corps of Engineers

1853–1858

Pacific Railroad surveys involved topographical engineers in detailed documentation of the West.

1857

Lieutenant Gouverneur K. Warren completed his map of the northern plains, the most detailed and accurate to date.

1861

Humphreys–Abbot *Report Upon the Physics and Hydraulics of the Mississippi River* argued that only levees were necessary to prevent flooding.

1861–1865

Civil War: A battalion of regular Army engineer troops with various volunteer engineer and pioneer units cleared obstacles, constructed roads and bridges, laid down ponton bridges, and erected field fortifications. Several engineer officers commanded combined troops while others conducted reconnaissance and directed siege operations.

1863

New Capitol dome completed under supervision of Montgomery C. Meigs.

5

1863

Army engineers constructed 2,200-foot ponton bridge over the James River, probably the longest ponton bridge in the history of warfare.

1863

Corps of Engineers and Corps of Topographical Engineers reunified.

1866

Engineer School of Application founded at Willet's Point, New York. Chief of Engineers' role as Inspector at West Point ended as superintendency of the academy opened to all branches of the Army.

1867

Control of District of Columbia public parks and monuments given to the Office of Public Buildings and Grounds under the Chief of Engineers.

1875

Captain William Ludlow's expedition to Yellowstone identified critical need to protect and improve the park.

1878

Three-person commission, including an engineer commissioner, replaced elected government in the District of Columbia.

1879

Mississippi River Commission created to execute a comprehensive flood control and navigation plan on the Lower Mississippi.

Ponton bridge across the James.

Falls in Yellowstone.

Major General Quincy A. Gillmore, first president of the Mississippi River Commission.

Workmen
pointing tip of
Washington
Monument.

Timber dam at
Leech Lake.

Library of
Congress under
construction,
1888.

Office of History, Corps of Engineers

Minnesota Historical Society

Public Affairs Office, Corps of Engineers

1882

In first authorized emergency operation, Corps used Mississippi fleet to deliver relief to flood victims.

1883

Congress designated Corps to make improvements in Yellowstone Park.

1884

Construction of Washington Monument completed.

1884

First Corps reservoirs completed at Winnibigoshish, Leech Lake, and Pokegama, Minnesota.

1885

Davis Island Lock and Dam just south of Pittsburgh completed as the largest chanoine wicket dam in the world.

1888

Chief of Engineers created five engineer divisions based on geographical regions.

1897

Library of Congress completed.

7

U.S. Army ferry in the Philippines.

1898

Spanish–American War: Army engineers erected landing piers, built bridges and roads, and repaired and operated railroads from Cuba and Puerto Rico to the Philippines.

1899

Refuse Act gave Corps authority to regulate obstructions to navigation.

1901

Engineer School moved from Willet's Point to Washington Barracks.

1902

Board of Engineers for Rivers and Harbors established to examine cost, benefits, and the need to improve waterways. (Disestablished in 1993.)

1911

Using revolutionary cofferdam design, Corps raised wreck of the battleship *Maine* in Havana harbor.

U S Military Academy Library

Culebra Cut, Panama Canal.

1914

Panama Canal completed under supervision of Army engineer officers.

1917

Congress passed first federal flood control act.

High water in Hickman, Kentucky, 1912.

Office of History, Corps of Engineers

8

Engineering
survey party
in Sussex,
England, 1918.

Installing Wilson
Dam power
generators.

Flooded streets
in Pine Bluff,
Arkansas,
1927.

1917–1918

World War I: Army engineers
served in combat; built ports,
roads, and railroads; organized
first U.S. Army tank units; and
developed chemical warfare
munitions.

1919

Engineer School moved to Camp
Humphreys (later renamed
Fort Belvoir).

1925

Wilson Dam completed with major
hydroelectric power component
at Muscle Shoals on the
Tennessee River.

1927

Congress authorized 308 Reports
to present plans for multipurpose
improvement of navigable
streams.

1927

Flood devastated Mississippi
River and demonstrated
insufficiency of "levees only"
policy.

9

1928

Jadwin Plan accepted for controlling flooding on the Mississippi using floodways and spillways in addition to levees.

1929

Nine-foot navigation project completed on the Ohio River.

1930s

Fort Peck, Bonneville, and Passamaquoddy projects constructed as part of New Deal public works program.

1936

Flood Control Act made flood control a federal policy and officially recognized the Corps as the major federal flood control agency.

1939

Nine-foot navigation project completed on the Upper Mississippi.

1940

Corps took over airfield construction from the Quartermaster Corps' Construction Division.

1941

Corps took over all real estate acquisition, construction, and maintenance for Army facilities.

1942

Manhattan Engineer District created to oversee construction of production facilities for the atomic bomb.

1942

Engineers completed a 1,500-mile pioneer road, called the Alaska or ALCAN Highway, between Dawson Creek, British Columbia, and Fairbanks, Alaska.

10

Major General Edgar Jadwin.

President Franklin D. Roosevelt inspects model of Passamaquoddy Tidal Power Project, Maine.

250-ton roller at work.

Clearing land for Alaska Highway.

Office of History, Corps of Engineers

Elephant-mounted
survey party and
bulldozer on the
Ledo Road, North
Burma

Office of History, Corps of Engineers

The dredge *Poseidon*
clearing the Corinth
Canal, 1947

Combat engineers
lay wire along
defense perimeter,
Korea, 1952.

Office of History, Corps of Engineers

Office of History, Corps of Engineers

1943

Construction of the Pentagon
completed 15 months after
groundbreaking.

1944

Flood Control Act authorized
Corps to develop recreation
facilities on Corps' projects and
to develop water projects in the
Missouri River Valley in
accordance with the
Pick–Sloan Plan.

1945

Construction, begun in late 1942,
completed on Ledo Road,
stretching through some of the
world's most difficult terrain from
the northeast corner of India to a
junction with the old Burma Road
near the Chinese border.

1946

Corps began hospital construction
program for the Veterans
Administration.

1946–1949

Corps' Grecian District supervised
postwar construction to restore
damaged Greek transportation
and communication network as
check on Soviet expansion.

1950–1953

Korean Conflict: Engineers
destroyed bridges and mined
roads to obstruct the enemy and
built bridges and roads to assist
advance of American forces.
Engineers frequently fought as
infantry.

1950s

Corps built early warning facilities and air bases in Greenland, Morocco, and Libya.

1952

Corps assigned responsibility for the Army Nuclear Power Program.

1958

Corps completed work on the American portion of the St. Lawrence Seaway.

1960 *(next page)*

Corps of Engineers Ballistic Missile Construction Office established to build launch sites and related facilities for intercontinental ballistic missiles.

1961

Foreign Assistance Act initiated Corps involvement in reimbursable programs through the State Department's Agency for International Development (AID).

12

Hangar at Nouasseur, Morocco, December 1952.

Office of History, Corps of Engineers

Construction of SM-1 Nuclear Power Plant, Fort Belvoir, Virginia.

Office of History, Corps of Engineers

Soo Locks, Sault Ste. Marie, Michigan, today.

Public Affairs Office, Corps of Engineers

Vehicle
Assembly
Building,
Saturn
complex 39.

Cincinnati
Bulk Mail
Center.

Titan II
silo.

 1961

Corps began construction support
for NASA leading to major
activities at the Manned
Spacecraft Center in Houston,
Texas, and John F. Kennedy
Space Center in Florida.

1962

In Army reorganization Corps lost
control of Engineer School and
engineer troops but retained
responsibility for engineering,
construction, and real estate
services required by the Army,
Air Force, and NASA.

1967

Rome Plow introduced to
enhance engineer jungle-clearing
operations during Vietnam War.

1970

National Environmental Policy Act,
signed on January 1, instituted
requirement for environmental
impact statements.

1971–1976

Corps constructed bulk-mail
handling centers for the U.S.
Postal Service.

1972

Clean Water Act of 1972 authorized Corps to regulate dredging
and dumping activities in U.S.
wetlands.

1975

Corps redesignated as a combat arms branch.

1975

First Assistant Secretary of the Army for Civil Works named to position originally created in 1970 legislation.

1976

Middle East Division established in Riyadh as Saudi construction program expanded. (Disestablished in 1986.)

Main mosque, King Abdul Aziz Military Academy, Saudi Arabia.

1979

Corps of Engineers became an Army major command (MACOM).

Distinctive unit insignia for U.S. Army Corps of Engineers.

1982

Design and construction effort begun in support of Environmental Protection Agency's Superfund cleanup program.

1982

Israeli air bases completed in program initiated in 1979 by Camp David Accords.

1983

Defense Environmental Restoration Program enlarged the Corps' environmental work relating to military installations.

Jet landing at Ovda Air Base.

14

Corps contractors
repair heavily
damaged power
lines, Kuwait, 1991.

Jonas Jordan, Savannah District

Tennessee–
Tombigbee's
Gainesville
spillway under
construction.

Public Affairs Office, Corps of Engineers

Mobile
home
destroyed
by
Hurricane
Andrew,
Homestead,
Florida,
1992.

Public Affairs Office, Corps of Engineers

1985

Tennessee–Tombigbee
Waterway, largest navigation
project in Corps' history,
completed 13 years after
construction started in 1972.

1986

Water Resources Development
Act brought major change in
financing by requiring nonfederal
contributions toward most federal
water resources projects.

1988

The Engineer School relocated to
Fort Leonard Wood, Missouri.

1990–1991

Corps provided contract construction and real estate support during
Desert Shield/Desert Storm.

1991

Recovery effort in Kuwait initiated
through the Kuwait Emergency
Recovery Office. Transatlantic
Division established in
Winchester, Virginia.

1992

Corps undertook major disaster
recovery in wake of Hurricane
Andrew and Hurricane Iniki.

1993

Assistant Chief of Staff/Installation
Management Office created on
Department of the Army staff.
This absorbed many of the
functions of the Assistant Chief of
Engineers.

1996

Official ground breaking ceremony
for the Olmsted Lock, the last major
lock modernization project on the
Ohio River in a program begun in
the 1950s.

15

The Revolutionary War

Washington assumes command at Cambridge, Massachusetts.

National Archives

Independence National Historical Park Collection

Major General Louis Duportail, by Charles Willson Peale.

French artist's lithograph portrays action at Yorktown.

When Congress organized the Continental Army on June 16, 1775, it provided for a Chief Engineer and two assistants with the Grand Army and a Chief Engineer and two assistants in a separate department, should one be established. Colonel Richard Gridley of Massachusetts, one of the few colonials with experience in the design and construction of batteries and fortifications, became General George Washington's first Chief Engineer. Another native of Massachusetts, Rufus Putnam, who succeeded Gridley as Chief Engineer in 1776, was one of his assistants while the Army remained in Boston.

From the start the predominantly defensive nature of the war convinced Washington he would need even more trained engineers, but he was continually frustrated in his efforts to find them. Qualified engineers were scarce because formal schooling in siegecraft, the erec-

tion of field fortifications, and technology was practically non-existent in America at the time. In response to Washington's plea for more engineers, Congress turned to France which was an enemy of Britain and the center of technical education in Europe. The French also had a long tradition of military engineering. Beginning in 1776 Frenchmen began to arrive in America to serve as engineers. Before the end of 1777 Congress had promoted one of them, Louis Duportail, to brigadier general and Chief Engineer, a position he held for the duration of the war. Frenchmen, joined by other foreigners, dominated the ranks of the engineers throughout the war.

When Duportail took command of the engineers he renewed the pressure begun by his predecessor to establish a permanent, separate and distinct engineering branch of the Army. His proposal included a provision for companies of engineer troops to be known as Sappers and

17

Bunker Hill, June 17, 1775,
by H. Charles McBarron.

U.S. Army Center of Military History

Plan of attack for Yorktown,
drawn by Jean Baptiste de
Gouvion, October 29, 1781.

Thaddeus Kosciuszko, by
Charles Willson Peale.

Independence National Historical Park Collection

Yorktown, October 14, 1781, by H. Charles McBarron.

Miners and to be officered by Americans. From their ranks would come the engineer officers to replace the French when they returned home.

On May 27, 1778, Congress finally authorized three companies of Sappers and Miners who were to receive instruction in erecting field works—a first step toward technical education—and were to direct fatigue parties, repair damaged works and erect new ones. Recruitment continued for more than two years with activation of the three companies on August 2, 1780. Meanwhile on March 11, 1779, Congress passed a resolution which formed the engineers in the Continental Army into the Corps of Engineers Duportail had sought.

Despite the shortage of engineers and the delay in forming companies of engineer troops, the Army's engineers made numerous contributions to the war. Engineer officers reconnoitered enemy positions and probable battlefields, wrote useful reports based on their observations, oversaw the construction of fortifications and drew detailed maps for commanders. Congress relieved some of the mapping burden when it appointed Robert Erskine as Geographer of the Army in 1777. Erskine and his successor, Simeon DeWitt, employed several assistants as did Thomas Hutchins, whom Congress appointed as Geographer for the Southern Army in 1780. Following this precedent, Congress added Topographical Engineers to the Corps of Engineers in 1813 and created a Topographical Bureau in the Engineer Department in 1818.

Engineer officers often took action which helped achieve decisive results. One such incident occurred during the siege of Boston. In February 1776, General Washington's council of war decided to draw the British out of Boston by erecting works on the unfortified Dorchester Heights. To achieve surprise the

Army needed to move quickly, but the ground was frozen more than a foot deep. Colonel Rufus Putnam, Washington's Chief Engineer, offered an innovative solution to the problem. He recommended using chandeliers—wooden frames filled with bundles of sticks—to raise the walls above ground. To the astonishment of the enemy, the Continentals erected the chandeliers in a single night (March 4-5). When it was determined three days later that the position could not be taken, the British found that their hold on Boston was no longer tenable and evacuated the city.

The next year Lt. Col. Thaddeus Kosciuszko, a native of Poland commissioned as an engineer officer in the Continental Army, placed obstructions that significantly impeded Burgoyne's advance toward Albany after the fall of Fort Ticonderoga. Later Kosciuszko helped design the network of defenses at West Point and in 1781 he was instrumental in allowing Nathaniel Greene's Southern Army to evade capture by the enemy. During the difficult winter months of 1777-1778, Washington followed Duportail's advice: wear down the British at Philadelphia while avoiding attack. This strategy helped preserve the Army.

The Corps of Engineers and its companies of Sappers and Miners enjoyed their finest hour in October 1781 at Yorktown, where Washington conducted a siege in the classical manner of Sebastien de Vauban, the great French master of siegecraft. Engineer officers, numbering 13 in the combined French and American armies, performed crucial reconnaissance, and with the 50 men in the Sappers and Miners, planned and executed field works. In addition the Sappers and Miners assembled fortification materials, erected gun platforms, transported cannon and ammunition, and cleared the way for the decisive in-

fantry assault on Redoubt 10. After the battle Washington cited Duportail for conduct which afforded "brilliant proofs of his military genius, and set the seal of his reputation."

When the Revolution ended in 1783, a debate followed on the nature of the peacetime establishment of the Army. Proposals regarding the engineers varied. They included a union of the engineers with the artillerists and the establishment of an academy to provide training. Retaining an engineer presence in the Army was seen as necessary by those who favored a centralized system of fortifications. Engineers would be needed to build and maintain them. Two arguments in favor of retaining the engineers drew directly upon Revolutionary War experience. Without a permanent, trained Corps of Engineers, it was maintained, the new nation would be forced to call on foreigners again in time of war. Moreover, as the Revolutionary War had demonstrated, it was extremely difficult to put together an effective technical organization in a short time. But Congress did not approve a peacetime Army and with that decision went any hope of retaining the Corps of Engineers. By the end of 1783 the Corps and its companies of Sappers and Miners had mustered out of service.

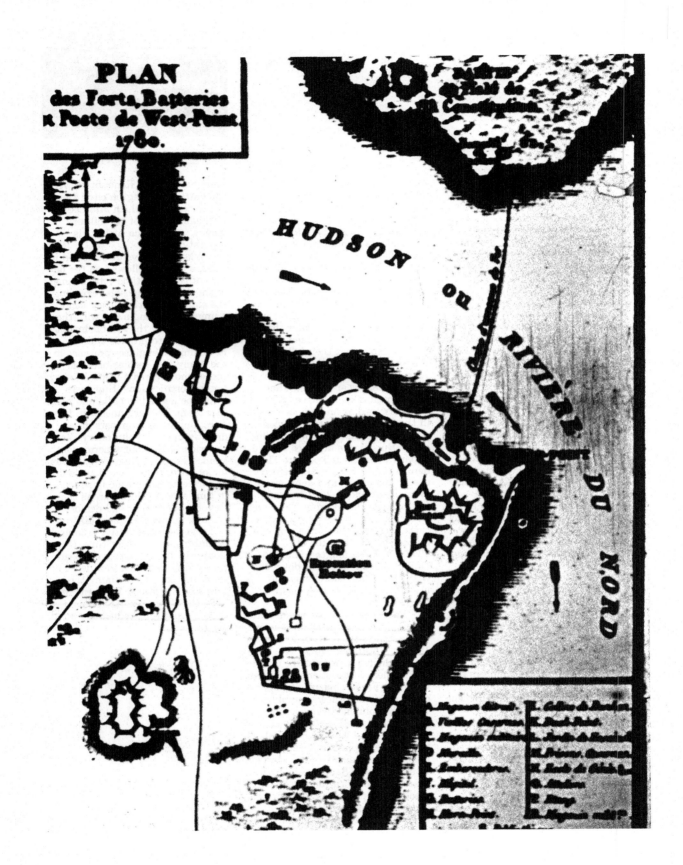

PLAN
des Forts, Batteries
et Poste de West-Point.
1780.

Union with the Artillerists

West Point in 1783. Wood engraving by C. Tiebout from a drawing by H. Livingston.

Likeness of Pierre Charles L'Enfant.

1780 plan for West Point.

When the new government under the Constitution was launched in 1789, Secretary of War Henry Knox recommended "a small corps of well-disciplined and well-informed artillerists and engineers." Nevertheless, no engineers served the Army until March 1794 when war threatened with Britain. At that time Congress authorized President Washington to appoint temporary engineers to direct the fortification of key harbors. Among those named were Pierre L'Enfant and Major Stephen Rochefontaine, another veteran of the Revolutionary War Corps of Engineers.

The following May, heeding the much earlier advice of Duportail and others, Congress established a single Corps of Artillerists and Engineers consisting of one regiment. Rochefontaine assumed command of the new Corps. At the same time a school to train Army officers took shape at West Point, New York.

As war threatened with France in 1798, Congress added a second regiment of artillerists and engineers. In 1802 Congress reduced the military establishment again and separated the artillerists and engineers. The union, which so many Revolutionary War Engineers had supported, was short-lived. Yet the Corps of Engineers survived the peacetime reduction and took charge of the military academy now established permanently at West Point.

The SCALE of PLANS of

FORT ERIE

L. ERIE

Engineers in the War of 1812

Plan of Fort McHenry.

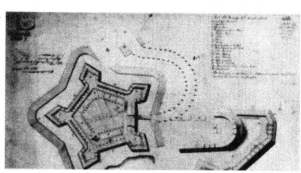

After the Revolution, engineer officers did not see combat again until the War of 1812. In that war their record was exceptional in comparison to the record of the other branches of the Army. When the war broke out in June, the Corps of Engineers' actual strength was only 17 officers and 19 enlisted men. Although Congress had authorized the Corps 22 officers and 113 enlisted men in April 1812, full strength was not approached until 1815. West Point graduates dominated the list of officers serving in the Corps and for all it was their first experience in combat.

During the years immediately preceding the conflict engineer officers had worked full-time constructing permanent defenses along the Atlantic coast. As the war progressed, the War Department increasingly transferred engineers to serve in the field on the Northern frontier. In combat the engineers performed many of the same tasks they had in the Revolution—constructing fortifications, reconnaissance and mapping and assisting the movement of armies. In at least two instances engineer officers directed construction of quarters. Still, fortifications were the primary concern of the engineers during the War of 1812 as they had been earlier. Despite the views of later critics, coastal harbors heavily fortified by the engineers did deter British attack. Notable examples of this were at Fort Meigs and Fort McHenry in Baltimore.

The War Department had debated with the engineers over their desire for command responsibility since 1802. Jonathan Williams, the first superintendent of West Point, had even resigned his position over the issue. During the War of 1812 engineer officers assumed command responsibility for the first time. Captain Charles Gratiot, later Chief Engineer, at one point commanded all forces in Michigan Territory. In 1813 Joseph G. Swift, another future Chief Engineer, commanded line units on Staten Island in addition to Fort Richmond and Hudson Battery. By late the next year he commanded the entire New York operation, which included more than 10,000 soldiers and civilian volunteers.

The performance of the Army engineers in combat between 1812 and 1815 helped them earn respectability and strengthened the military academy at West Point, which had been languishing on the eve of the war. While many battles in this indecisive war ended in a stand-off, the results might have been far worse without the contributions of the Army engineers.

Battle of Lundy's Lane, where Army engineers figured prominently, July 1814.

Map of Fort Erie depicting how Army engineers changed the old British fort into a bastion.

23

The Corps and the Military Academy at West Point, 1802-1866

Early West Point class.

Early view of West Point.

Portrayal of West Point
student at work.

During the American Revolution many officers, including General George Washington, the commander in chief, saw the need for technical education so that the Army would have skilled, native American engineer officers in the future. When Congress established the companies of Sappers and Miners in 1778, it stated that the companies were to receive instruction in field works. In subsequent general orders Washington referred to the Sappers and Miners as "a school of engineering." Regulations issued in 1779 for the Corps of Engineers and companies of Sappers and Miners declared that the Sappers and Miners were to receive instruction at times when they were not exercising duties. The chief engineer was to devise an instructional program and appoint engineer officers to give lectures. The amount of education actually given the Sappers and

Miners during the Revolution was minimal.

During the debate over a peacetime military establishment in 1783, several Army officers proposed establishing an academy at West Point either as the sole military academy or as one of several academies. Engineers particularly were thought to need formal training. When Congress decided against a peacetime standing Army, the need for an academy disappeared.

Some instruction did occur at West Point from 1794 until 1796, but it was not until March 16, 1802, that Congress reestablished a separate Corps of Engineers and constituted the Corps as the Military Academy. As Chief Engineer, Jonathan Williams, grand-nephew of Benjamin Franklin and a man keenly interested in the development of science, became the Academy's first superintendent. Williams introduced

25

U.S. Military Academy
class of 1904 cadets
working with models.

West Point, from a L'Enfant
watercolor.

Reenactment of West Point
classroom instruction.

Dennis H. Mahan.

new texts from England and the continent and by 1808 had broadened the curriculum from its heavy emphasis on mathematics to include engineering. In 1812 Congress created a professorship of engineering at the Academy. It was the first such position at an institution of higher learning in the United States.

Major advances in the organization and the course of study, as well as an honor code and a disciplinary system, followed under Sylvanus Thayer, superintendent from 1817 until 1833. Thayer patterned the reorganization of the Academy on the program he observed at the Ecole Polytechnique while on a visit to France. Claudius Crozet, who occupied the professorship of engineer-

(1836) and the *Course of Civil Engineering*, which first appeared in 1837.

In 1800 Secretary of War James McHenry had emphasized that fortification was only one part of the engineering profession. The engineer's utility, he declared, "extends to almost every Department of War; besides embracing whatever respects public buildings, roads, bridges, canals and all such works of a civil nature." After the War of 1812 West Point exemplified McHenry's dictum. The Academy was the first school of engineering in America and for many years produced graduates who played a major role in the internal improvement of the nation.

The Military Academy contin-

ing from 1817-1823 and was a graduate of the Ecole Polytechnique, introduced numerous French texts in his courses. Later, under Dennis Hart Mahan, the Academy's reputation as a school of civil engineering advanced still further. In his lectures Mahan, an 1824 graduate with a commission in the Corps of Engineers, drew upon his experiences while on duty in Europe (1826-1830). He prepared and added several texts to the West Point curriculum. The most important were *A Treatise on Field Fortification*

ued under the supervision of the Corps of Engineers until 1866, when Congress opened the superintendency to all branches of the Army and placed control of the Academy under the secretary of war, thus ending the Chief of Engineers' role as Inspector. This change responded in part to the fact that the Academy supported the entire Army, not just the engineers. Mathematics, science and engineering remained at the center of the curriculum.

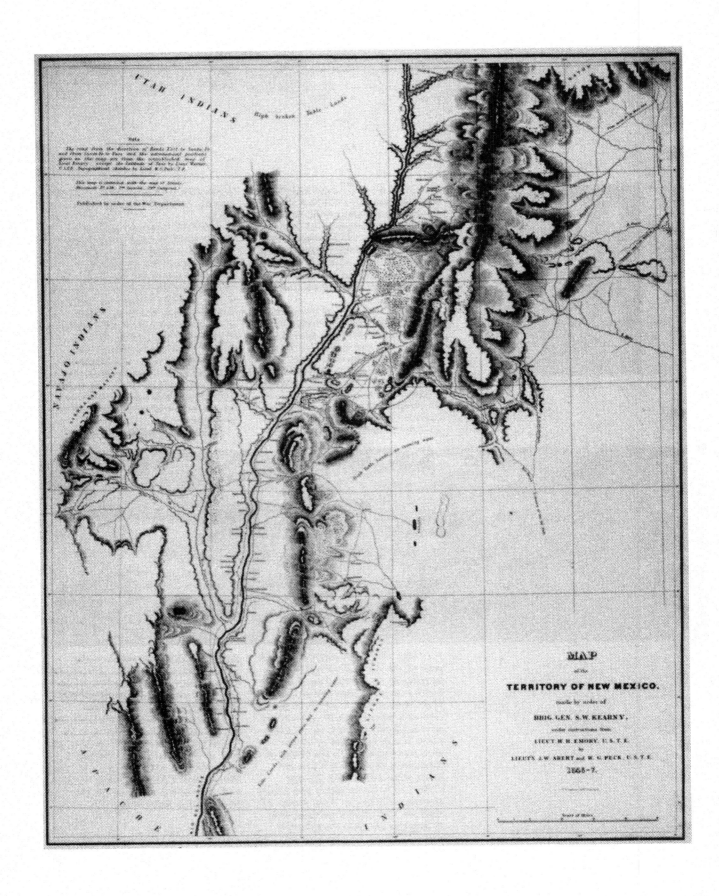

MAP

of the

TERRITORY OF NEW MEXICO.

made by order of

BRIG. GEN. S. W. KEARNY,

under instructions from

LIEUT. W. H. EMORY, U. S. T. E.

by

LIEUTS. J. W. ABERT and W. G. PECK, U. S. T. E.

1846-7.

Explorations and Surveys

View of the insulated table lands at the foot of the Rocky Mountains.

Library of Congress

Survey party at work.

Office of History, Corps of Engineers

Map of the Rio Grande Valley, drawn in 1846-47 for Mexican War reconnaissance.

Although the reconnaissance of the trans-Mississippi West began with the epic journey of Lewis and Clark in 1804-1806, another 10 years passed before the government began to establish the basis for the professionalization of official exploration. In 1816 topographical officers, known as geographers during the Revolution and as topographical engineers during the War of 1812 and thereafter, were added to the peacetime Army. Unlike the other officers of the Corps of Engineers, whose primarily military duties centered on the construction and maintenance of fortifications, "topogs" performed essentially civil tasks as surveyors, explorers and cartographers. Two years later the War Department established the Topographical Bureau under Major Isaac Roberdeau to collect and store the maps and reports of topographical operations. Like the topogs, who numbered only six at this early date, the bureau was placed under the Engineer Department.

Almost from the outset there was a great demand for the skills of the topographical engineers. The accelerated movement of Americans into the interior of the continent served to emphasize the nation's need for networks of transportation and communication. Congress

recognized the compelling nature of the requirement in 1824 by passage of the General Survey Act. This law, which authorized surveys for a national network of internal improvements, became the basis for topog involvement in the development of canals, roads and later, railroads.

Along with the growing importance of the topogs came increases in their numbers and improvements in the organizational structure. Most of the changes came during the first decade of Colonel John J. Abert's tenure as Chief of the Topographical Bureau. A strong-willed and ambitious West Pointer who received the appointment after Roberdeau died in 1829, Abert sought independence for both the bureau and the topogs. He realized the first goal in 1831, when Congress removed the bureau from the Engineer Department and gave it departmental status under the secretary of war. Seven years later he attained the second objective and became Chief of an independent Corps of Topographical Engineers, a position he held for 23 years.

Colonel Abert sought a great deal more for the topogs than prominence within the bureaucracy. While Roberdeau had been content to manage the office as a depot for maps and instruments and as a

Sciurus Aberti, squirrel named for John J. Abert, drawn by Richard H. Kern.

clearinghouse for correspondence, Abert saw his role as a planner and administrator for national policy regarding internal improvements and western exploration. As a member of the Board of Engineers for Internal Improvements, established to evaluate projects considered under the General Survey Act, Abert had a part in the selection of tasks and their execution. In western exploration, which for many years took a back seat to internal improvements, Abert's role remained minor. His bureau distributed instruments, collected maps and forwarded correspondence.

Individual members of the Corps of Topographical Engineers, however, achieved great importance in western exploration and surveys. During the expansionist era of the 1840s, from the first stirrings of Oregon fever in the early years of the decade to the acquisition of the huge southwestern domain after the Mexican War, topogs examined the

new country and reported their findings to a populace eager for information about the lands, native peoples and resources of the West. Best known of all was John C. Frémont, the dark-eyed and flamboyant Pathfinder who led three parties to the Rockies and beyond during this age of expansion. The ranks also included William H. Emory, author of a perceptive assessment of the Southwest, and James H. Simpson, discoverer of the ruins of the ancient Pueblo civilization of New Mexico. Howard Stansbury, whose report of an exploration of the Great Salt Lake is still considered a frontier classic, also wore the gold braid of the Corps of Topographical Engineers. In the 1850s, when the emphasis shifted from reconnaissance to more detailed exploration and roadbuilding, topogs continued to make their marks. John N. Macomb laid out the basic road network of New Mexico and George H. Derby initiated harbor improve-

ments in California, while Joseph C. Ives became the first Anglo-American to descend the Grand Canyon.

The disparity between the renown of members of Abert's Corps and the obscurity of his bureau was due to the absence of a government policy regarding exploration. Topographical engineers frequently went into the new country on an *ad hoc* basis, at the behest of a politically powerful figure like Missouri Senator Thomas Hart Benton, or to accompany a military expedition. From Major Stephen H. Long's 1819 journey up the Missouri River as a minor adjunct of Colonel Henry Atkinson's Yellowstone Expedition to Emory's Southwestern Exploration with the Army of the West during the Mexican War, topog exploration often took a secondary position to other purposes.

When exploration and surveys in the trans-Mississippi West were finally organized and coordinated in the 1850s, Abert no longer wielded the political influence that had brought his ambitions so near fruition in the 1830s. Duties he hoped would devolve on the Topographical Bureau went instead to the Office of Pacific Railroad Explorations and Surveys. This small organization, created by Abert's political foe, Secretary of War Jefferson Davis, managed the surveys for railroad routes to the Pacific Ocean. Of the leaders of the survey parties, only former engineer Isaac I. Stevens was not a topog. The railroad surveys produced a multi-volume report that was a veritable encyclopedia of trans-Mississippi natural history as well as reconnaissances of future railroad routes to the Pacific.

Despite the lack of a unified policy and central direction, the history of topog expeditions forms a coherent entity. Topographical officers provided the necessary link between the first explorations of the mountainmen—those rude, brawling

Pacific railroad survey party camped in the Mohave Valley.

Los Angeles in the 1850s as seen by a Pacific Railroad Survey party.

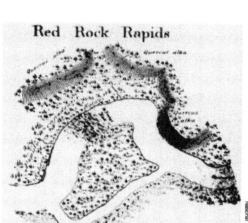

Red Rock Rapids

A portion of John C. Fremont's 1841 map of the Des Moines River.

beaver trappers who first probed far beyond the frontier and were no less than walking storehouses of geographical knowledge—and the civilian scientific specialists who undertook a rigorous study of western natural history and resources after the Civil War. Between the trappers and the specialists of the United States Geological Service, topogs provided the nation with an overall picture of the trans-Mississippi region. They explored bits and pieces as opportunity allowed until a coherent general understanding of western topography emerged in the form of Lieutenant Gouverneur K. Warren's map of 1858. His achievement, the first accurate overall depiction of the trans-Mississippi West, was a milestone in American cartography. Thereafter, topog activity centered on filling in the few blank spaces in Warren's map. During the Civil War, the Corps of Topographical Engineers was merged into the Corps of Engineers, whose officers renewed the topogs' efforts after Appomattox. Within a few years, however, civilian scientists took over the work and carried it forward. By then the officer-explorers had done their major task. They had extended and codified the knowledge of the mountainmen and in turn laid the groundwork for scholarly analysis. The topographical engineers had performed an essential service to a nation growing in size and in self-understanding.

Engineer Observations of the Aurora Borealis

While exploring and surveying the American West in the 19th century, Army engineers and topographers amassed a wealth of scientific information. Their concerns included archeology, astronomy, botany, biology and meteorology. Little known are a series of astronomical observations made by engineer officers undergoing training at the Engineer School of Application at Willets Point, New York, in the 1870s and 1880s.

The engineers made the bulk of their studies from an observatory constructed on the post in 1868. A new observatory boasting telescopes, transits, chronometers and chronographs opened in September 1879. The officers calculated longitude and latitude utilizing the sun, moon, stars and planets. In the course of their training exercises, which supplemented classroom work, the students had the opportunity to observe and record unusual phenomena. Such was the case in a series of systematic field observations of the *aurora borealis* begun in February 1870 and continued through 1884.

The engineers made the auroral observations purposely in an effort to determine the relation-

ship between auroral displays and the frequency of sunspots and magnetic disturbances. Sentinels from the engineer battalion on duty from sunset to sunrise at three guard posts recorded all visual sightings, noting whether skies were clear or cloudy. To account for human error, especially for the difficulty of identifying fainter displays, the battalion compiled tables noting the three independent observations, calculating a mean average and estimating the number of displays that might have occurred on cloudy nights. Officers stationed at the engineer supply depots at Washington Barracks, Missouri, and at Yerba Buena Island in San Francisco Bay also made their own less detailed observations, which in turn were compared with those at Willets Point.

While records of sunspot activity were not kept systematically, the battalion commander concluded from data available that the years of maximum and minimum sunspot activity corresponded with maximum and minimum auroral displays. The auroral statistics gathered at Willets Point are the earliest available and today continue to be useful to scientists studying the recurrence of the *aurora* and its relationship to sunspot activity.

31

The National Road

Conestoga wagons crossing the Appalachian Mountains on the National Road.

The tubular-arch bridge over Dunlap's Creek in Pennsylvania built by engineer Captain Richard Delafield for the National Road. It was the first cast-iron bridge in the United States.

Traveling on the National Road, 1939.

As pioneers and immigrants settled west of the Appalachian Mountains, Americans felt a pressing need for reliable transportation routes to the newly formed states in the Ohio and Mississippi River basins. President Jefferson's Secretary of the Treasury Albert Gallatin and others proposed many road and river improvement projects to meet this need, but before 1840 only one received very substantial federal financial support. This was the National Road between Cumberland, Maryland, and Vandalia, Illinois, which the government built in 1811-1841 at a cost of over $6 million.

Gallatin's Treasury Department supervised the construction of the first segment of the road, built between Cumberland on the Potomac River and Wheeling on the Ohio River in 1811-1818. The Corps of Engineers was given direction of the road's construction in 1825 when Congress authorized the continuation of the road west of the Ohio. The Secretary of War then ordered that the road be constructed following the method introduced in England by John McAdam. McAdam had found that applying three successive 3-inch layers of broken stone above ground level produced a well-compacted road surface that could bear the heaviest contemporary loads. Civilian superintendents reporting to the Engineer Department oversaw the road's construction until Congress, in 1832-1834, mandated that engineer officers be placed in immediate charge.

By then the road east of the Ohio River had fallen into serious disrepair, and Congress ordered that an engineer officer fix it and then turn it over for maintenance to the states through which it passed. That section of the road had been built with large foundation stones, and many of these had worked their way to the surface at dangerous angles. In return for subsequent state assumption of maintenance responsibilities, the federal government agreed to macadamize the road, to build a new route just west of Cumberland that avoided a steep mountain ridge, and to replace several decaying original bridges.

Engineer Captain Richard Delafield, a future Chief of Engineers, supervised most of the eastern repair work. His solid, new masonry bridge over Will's Creek west of Cumberland had two elliptical arches each spanning 59 feet and standing more than 26 feet above the water. With wing walls, its total length was 291 feet. He built across Dunlap's Creek at Brownsville, Pennsylvania, the first bridge with a cast-iron superstructure constructed in the United States, an 80-foot long span that remains in use today. The Cumberland Road project was an early example of the Corps of Engineers providing imaginative and durable engineering work under challenging circumstances.

3 41sr.

Minots Ledge Lighthouse
Wednesday, August 3, 1857.

Lighthouses

Cape Lookout Lighthouse, North Carolina.

Proposed iron screw-pile lighthouse for Chicago Harbor.

Building Minot's Ledge lighthouse off Cohasset, Massachusetts, August 3, 1859.

As early as 1716 on the Atlantic Coast, private parties built lighthouses. Army engineers began supervising lighthouse construction in 1827. In 1831, the Treasury Department placed funds appropriated for lighthouses in the hands of the Chief Engineer. A federal Lighthouse Board, created in 1852, assumed the responsibility for supervising lighthouse construction and inspection. Three engineer officers were members of the original Lighthouse Board. They continued to serve as board members and as lighthouse district inspectors and engineers until Congress abolished the Lighthouse Board in 1910. Since then, engineer officers have undertaken some lighthouse work assignments but not on a regular basis.

In the 19th century, engineer officers designed lighthouses to help mariners weather violent Atlantic storms. Adopting European technology, those officers often innovated to solve particular problems. Major Hartman Bache borrowed from the British engineers the design for the first screw-pile lighthouse in the United States. This type of pile was ideal for the bottom of the Delaware Bay, since it could be securely twisted into an unstable sea floor. To fend off the floating ice that threatened a structure at Brandywine Shoal, Delaware, Bache installed a fence, consisting of screwpiles, five inches in diameter, around the lighthouse. He then added an outer fence and the space between the two fences was platformed over. Tons of stone riprap were dumped around the structure to provide additional protection. Engineering advances later made it possible to erect sturdy lighthouses on the reefs around the Florida Keys, the most famous of these being the Sombrero Key lighthouse, built by Lieutenant George Meade seven years before he met General Robert E. Lee at Gettysburg in July 1863.

Origins of Civil
Works Missions

Engineers aid in railroad
construction, c.1880.

John C. Calhoun, by John
Wesley Jarvis.

U.S. Snagboat No. 2,
similar to those constructed
in the 1840s and 1850s,
from *Harper's Weekly*,
November 2, 1889.

One of the major lessons of the War of 1812 was that the nation needed an improved defense and transportation system. The British had invaded the country from the north, from the south at New Orleans, and from the east, marching inland and even putting the capital to the torch. In the 1816 mobilization studies based upon the lessons of the War of 1812, the Corps of Engineers reported that national defense should rest upon four pillars: a strong Navy at sea; a highly mobile regular Army supported by reserves and National Guard; invincible defenses on the seacoasts; and improved rivers, harbors and transportation systems that would permit rapid armed concentration against an invading enemy and swifter, more economical logistical lines.

In 1819 John C. Calhoun, then secretary of war, recommended that the Corps of Engineers be directed to improve waterways navigation and other transportation systems because such civil works projects would facilitate the movement of the Army and its materials while contributing to national economic development. "It is in a state of war when a nation is compelled to put all of its resources . . . into requisition," said Calhoun, "that its Government realizes in its security the beneficial effects from a people made prosperous by a wise direction of its resources in peacetime."

Congress finally accepted Calhoun's recommendations in 1824.

Snagboat clearing debris.

U.S. Steamer *Aid* battles raft no. 5 on the Red River.

U.S. Dredge *Harwood* at Milton's Bluff, Muscle Shoals, Alabama, May 1889.

Early steamers on the
Ohio, c.1820.

Heights of Fame and Fortune,
by Frederick B. Read, 1873

"A Globe of Compression":
Brigadier General Joseph G.
Swift and the New York Fire of
1835

Long before the Corps as an
organization was charged with
aiding victims of natural disasters, Army engineers as individuals lent a helping hand to fellow
citizens in time of trouble. An
early example of the engineer as
good samaritan was provided by
Brigadier General Joseph G.
Swift, former Chief Engineer, during the great New York fire of
1835.

Fire broke out in lower Manhattan on December 16 of that year.
It spread rapidly, consuming
houses and stores. The blaze
threatened to devour the entire
city.

Alarmed and desperate, the
New York City mayor turned to
General Swift, a municipal hero
since 1814, when he directed the
city's defense against threatened
British attack. At the time of the
fire, Swift was retired from the
Army and working as a civilian
on harbor improvements for the
Corps. Swift decided to contain
the blaze behind a line of purposely demolished buildings. He
calculated how much gun powder
would be needed to "shake
down" a house without damaging
neighboring properties. Then he
directed the placing of the
charges in such a way to create
"a globe of compression" when
ignited. As the powder went off,
walls toppled inward and houses
collapsed in ruins upon themselves, leaving adjacent structures unharmed. A novelty at the
time, this technique is now common practice in the urban demolition business.

At great personal risk, Swift set
off charge after charge, arresting
the fire's advance on December
17 and thus saving countless
lives and millions of dollars in
property. For the second time in
two decades, he received the
city's official thanks.

It passed a General Survey Act on
April 30 that authorized the President to use Army engineers to
survey road and canal routes "of
national importance, in a commercial or military point of view." A few
weeks later, on May 24, Congress
appropriated $75,000 for improving
navigation on the Ohio and Mississippi rivers. This law allowed the
President to employ "any of the engineers in the public service which
he may deem proper" for the work.

Under the May 24 act, the Corps
began to remove snags and floating
trees from the Ohio and Mississippi
rivers and to improve the Ohio's
channel by attacking the sandbars
that impeded river commerce. By
1829 Army engineers were using
snagboats developed by the famous
steamboat captain Henry M. Shreve
to remove obstructions in river channels. This early activity marked the
beginning of the Corps' civil works
mission—a dual role that emphasized a practical blending of civil
works and military skills and fos-
tered the development of a federal
agency prepared to shoulder the engineering burden in the event of war
or national emergency.

Louisville and Portland
Canal under construction,
1871.

Public Affairs Office, Corps of Engineers

Waterway Development

The first Corps of Engineers' dredge *Essayons* at the mouth of the Mississippi, c. 1870.

Excavating the Illinois and Mississippi Canal, 1904.

Launching the new dredge *Essayons*, 1982.

Benjamin Henry Latrobe, a famous early 19th century engineer, once remarked that "nothing is so easily converted to a civil use, as the science common both to the profession of a civil and military engineer." Few of Latrobe's contemporaries questioned this observation; engineers were also scientists and navigation improvements required a scientific approach utilizing principles developed mainly in Europe. At West Point, Army engineers learned the principles and applied them in their surveys of navigable rivers, often making their own significant contributions to river hydraulics in the process. In the early 1820s, Corps of Engineers officers surveyed both the Ohio and lower Mississippi

rivers. In the succeeding years many more rivers were investigated. Many early navigation improvements resulted from trial and error, however, rather than from strict adherence to theory. If the obvious did not work, the less obvious was used, until some method seemed to produce the desired result. A good example is the work on the Ohio River.

In 1824 Chief Engineer Alexander Macomb dispatched Major Stephen H. Long to the Ohio to initiate experiments to provide safer navigation. The major challenge was to deepen channels across sand and gravel bars. Long decided to perform experiments on a compacted gravel bar near Henderson, Kentucky, just below the mouth of

41

Sketch showing position
of dam and sandbar on the
Ohio, 1825.

Brevet Major General
Gouverneur K. Warren.

Ladder bucket dredge at work.

the Green River. At low river stage, this bar was covered by only 15 inches of water. After preliminary studies, the major outfitted several flatboats with hand-powered pile drivers and began to build a wing dam, so-called because the structure extended from the bank of the river at a 45 degree angle. The dams decreased the width of the channel, thereby increasing the current's velocity. Theoretically, this would cause the river to scour a deeper channel. Long built the dam to various widths, lengths and heights. The final structure was 402 yards long and consisted of twin rows of 1,400 piles joined with stringers and filled with brush. Sediment gathered against the dam and helped anchor it to the riverbed. The

project's total cost was $3,378.93.

Wing dams such as Long's were used on the Ohio and other major rivers during most of the 19th century, but their effectiveness was always marginal. They were easily destroyed and did not always produce the desired results. After the Civil War, Corps officers grew increasingly skeptical about the dams. Brevet Major General Gouverneur K. Warren, a well-respected engineer officer, candidly wrote in 1867, "I do not believe the country will ever stand such a heavy continuous outlay as the wing-dam system of the Ohio has caused, and I believe that the extravagant and useless expenditure there, in the palmy days of western river improvements between 1830 and 1844, did more than anything else to bring the whole subject into disrepute."

Warren's pessimism was unjustified, for both Congress and commercial interests continued to support waterway improvements after the Civil War. Indeed, the support increased. Rivers and harbors work jumped from about $3.5 million for 49 projects and 26 surveys in 1866 to nearly $19 million for 371 projects and 135 surveys in 1882. Nevertheless, Warren's frustration was shared by other engineers. W. Milnor Roberts, a well-known civil engineer, concluded in 1870 that existing navigation facilities on the Ohio, while certainly of public benefit, were no better than an "amelioration of the present difficulty." He proposed instead to canalize the river through the construction of 66 locks and dams. This project would offer six-foot slackwater navigation from Pittsburgh, Pennsylvania, to Cairo, Illinois.

Chief of Engineers Andrew A. Humphreys organized an Army Engineer Board of Inquiry, composed of Majors William E. Merrill and Godfrey Weitzel, to examine the question of canalizing the Ohio. The

Steamboats line the St. Louis waterfront, 1909.

National Archives

Lt. Eugene A. Woodruff: "A Model for all Similar Undertakings . . ."

In 1873 Captain Charles W. Howell, district engineer at New Orleans, assigned his deputy, Lieutenant Eugene A. Woodruff, to the Red River of Louisiana as supervisor of the project to clear the river of the great log raft, a formidable obstruction to navigation. In September of that year Lieutenant Woodruff left his workboats and crew on the Red River to visit Shreveport and recruit a survey party. When he arrived, he found Shreveport in the grip of a yellow fever epidemic. Fearing that he might carry the disease to his workmen if he returned to camp, Woodruff elected to remain in Shreveport and tend to the sick. Volunteering his services to the Howard Association, a Louisiana disaster relief charity, he traveled from house to house in his carriage, delivering food, medicine, and good cheer to the sick and dying. He contracted the disease and died of it in Shreveport on September 30.

"He died because too brave to abandon his post even in the face of a fearful pestilence and too humane to let his fellow beings perish without giving all the aid in his power to save them. His name should be cherished, not only by his many personal friends, but by the Army, as of one who lived purely, labored faithfully, and died in the path of duty. . . . His conduct of the great work on which he was engaged at the time of his death will be a model for all similar undertakings and the completion of the work a monument to his memory," wrote Captain Howell.

Howell then assigned the task of completing the work on the Red River to Assistant Engineer George Woodruff, the lieutenant's brother. On November 27, 1873, the Engineers broke through the raft, finally clearing the Red River for navigation.

officers agreed with Roberts that a system of locks and dams would best provide for future navigation. Somewhat surprisingly, the recommendation met resistance from the very group which would most profit from its implementation. Coal shippers, in Merrill's words, were "absolutely opposed to a slack-water system, unless arrangements can be made to pass their fleets through without stopping and separating for the passage of locks."

The resistance forced Merrill, who was in charge of Ohio River improvements, to look for alternative solutions. He thought the wicket dam design developed by Jacques Chanoine in France in 1852 might be adapted for use on the Ohio. The structure utilized a num-

U.S. Military Academy Library

ber of large folding boards, called wickets, which were hinged to a concrete base at the bottom of the river. Each wicket was about 3-3/4 feet wide and 12 feet long. When the wickets were raised, the water behind them rose high enough to insure navigation. During high water they could be lowered to allow boats to pass unimpeded. In this way, the delays the coal shippers feared would be avoided.

In 1874 Merrill proposed that a series of movable dams, employing Chanoine wickets, be constructed on the Ohio. For the first step, he recommended that a 110 by 600-foot lock and movable dam be built at Davis Island, five miles below Pittsburgh. In 1877 Congress approved Merrill's plan. A year later, the

Log raft on the Red River.

Placing bank protection along the Arkansas River near Pine Bluff, 1881.

The Davis Island Lock dedication, October 7, 1885.

Corps began construction of the Davis Island project, completing it seven years later. The 110 by 600-foot lock was the largest in the world, as was the 1,223-foot-long dam. The dam was actually composed of 305 separate Chanoine wickets and three weirs.

Impressed by the early success of the Davis Island project, in 1888 Congress authorized the extension of the six-foot navigation project down the Ohio. By 1904 two locks and dams had been completed, seven were under construction and five more were funded. At this time, before further work was done, Chief of Engineers Alexander Mackenzie decided to conduct another complete review of the project. The basic question was whether the project should be extended down the lower Ohio River, particularly in view of generally declining commerce on inland waterways.

Pursuant to congressional authorization, Mackenzie appointed a board headed by Colonel Daniel W. Lockwood and therefore called the Lockwood Board. Its review of the Ohio River project led to recommendations for a nine-foot project for the entire course of the Ohio. This conclusion rested on the finding that the probable cost per ton-mile for a six-foot project would be nearly fifty percent greater than for the nine-foot project. In the 1910 Rivers and Harbors Act, Congress authorized the construction of a nine-foot Ohio River canalization

project. At a cost of about $125 million, the project was completed in 1929.

Meanwhile, the Corps had been busy in other parts of the country developing a reliable internal waterway system. One of the key projects, going back to the mid-19th century, was the Soo Locks at Sault St. Marie, Michigan. These locks were instrumental in securing a navigable route from the copper and iron mines on the shores of Lake Superior to the industrial plants of the East. In 1852 Congress agreed to help private interests finance the cost of building a canal at St. Marys Falls to replace a structure on the Canadian side that had been destroyed during the War of 1812. Congressional participation involved granting 750,000 acres of land to the state of Michigan. Captain August Canfield of the topographical engineers was assigned as chief engineer and superintendent of the project for the state of Michigan. Canfield's design for the canal conformed to the congressional stipulation that the passage should be not less than 100 feet in width and 12 feet deep, with two locks not less than 250 feet long and 60 feet wide.

Within two decades, burgeoning traffic and larger vessels made the original canal inadequate to serve commercial needs, so Congress authorized the deepening of the St. Marys River channel and the construction of a new facility—the Weitzel Lock. Corps work began on July 11, 1870, with the appropriation of $150,000. The original canal was widened, varying from 50 to 108 feet, the depth increased from 12 to 16 feet, and the Corps constructed a lock 515 feet long by 80 feet wide with a lift of 17 feet.

At the time of its construction, the Weitzel Lock was considered to be the latest in lock technology. Its culvert valves, of the butterfly type, were operated by a single stroke hydraulic engine directly connected

to the valves. Hydraulic turbines generated the power which operated the lock gates. A movable dam was also introduced to shut off the flow of water during maintenance operations.

The Army's success in providing a passage to Lake Superior and Canada's commitment to canal building whetted the desires of shippers and industrialists for a deep water route through the Great Lakes—a dream eventually realized in the 20th century with the completion of the St. Lawrence Seaway.

It was the turn of the century when Congress responded to the renewed interest in water transportation by authorizing navigation projects designed to create an integrated system connecting inland areas with coastal harbors. Sandbars and rapids along the Ohio, Missouri, Arkansas and other major rivers posed major obstacles to the maintenance of year-round navigation channels. Eventually, with the advancement of lock and dam technology and more efficient dredging equipment, a nine-foot channel depth was assured in the Mississippi and its major tributaries.

Corps of Engineers navigation projects continue to play an important role in support of America's economic well-being. Commercial use of the 12,000 miles of inland and intracoastal waterways has increased: approximately one-sixth of all intercity cargo is transported by water. Waterborne commerce, recognized by experts to be the least expensive and least energy-consumptive means of transportation, is the logical choice for shippers of energy-producing commodities. Petroleum and coal together comprise more than half of all waterborne freight on the federally maintained waterways.

This expansion has been facilitated by the Corps' work on major waterways, including locks and dams. The Corps dredges more

Mixing plant on the Illinois and Mississippi Canal, 1900.

Engineer as Steamboat Designer
Colonel Stephen H. Long, an engineer officer famous for his exploration of the American West and for the survey and construction of early American railroads, also designed his own steamboat. In 1818, Long planned the building of the experimental craft, the *Western Engineer*, to transport himself and a task force of scientists, naturalists and artists as far west as possible by water on their projected trip into the frontier. The result was a steamboat designed to navigate narrow, shallow, snag-littered channels of inland rivers. It contained a particularly strong engine to provide increased power for pushing against swift currents. Another novel feature was a paddlewheel built into the stern to reduce the danger of damage from snags. The boat had a 75 by 13-foot hull with the weight of the machinery carefully distributed to permit increased maneuverability in shallow channels.

Altogether the *Western Engineer* was anything but a typical steamer. In fact, when launched in May 1819, its appearance was fearful—"Huge, black, scaly, the gigantic serpent blasted steam from its gaping mouth as it thrashed down the Ohio River, white foam dashing violently behind." In order to protect the vessel from Indian attack, Long installed a bulletproof pilot house. In addition, he had a cannon mounted on the bow, placed howitzers along the sides, and armed the crew with rifles and sabres. The boat had a serpent-like shape to frighten any would-be attackers.

The *Western Engineer*, drawing but 19 inches of water compared to the five or six feet of most steamboats, became the prototype of the western river steam vessels. In it, Long and his crew explored the Ohio River and ascended the Mississippi and Missouri rivers into Nebraska. On his journey, Long's *Western Engineer* traveled farther west than any other steamboat.

than 300 million cubic yards of material annually in order to maintain authorized channel depths and constructs bank stabilization projects in its traditional role as the primary developer of the nation's waterways. Also, as of 1996, engineer districts and divisions owned or operated 275 lock chambers at 230 sites. The oldest operating locks are Locks 1 and 2, which were built on the Kentucky River in 1839. The nation's newest locks opened in December 1994 and included the Joe D. Waggoner Lock and the Russell B. Long Lock on the Red River. An efficient system of interconnected waterways has proven to be a key factor in America's ability to mobilize in the event of war.

Soo Locks

Flood Control

Early levee construction.

Fascine matting on a
Mississippi River levee,
1885.

Flood refugees flee to
the levees in Hickman,
Kentucky, 1912.

Congress did not authorize a comprehensive topographic and hydrographic study of a major river basin until 1850, when floods along the Mississippi River drew congressional attention to the need for a practical plan for flood control and navigation improvements at the river's mouth. The Secretary of War, Charles M. Conrad, sent Lieutenant Colonel Stephen H. Long and Captain Andrew A. Humphreys, two officers of the Corps of Topographical Engineers, to the Mississippi basin to conduct the survey. Charles S. Ellet, Jr., one of the best-known engineers of the day, also applied to make the delta survey. Conrad suggested that Ellet work with Long and Humphreys, but Ellet preferred to work

independently. Under pressure from some congressmen and after seeing President Millard Fillmore, Conrad relented, dividing the $50,000 congressional appropriation between the Army survey and Ellet's.

Before the Army survey was complete, Humphreys became quite ill and had to quit. Long drafted a report based on Humphreys' notes, but he confined it simply to an exposition of what had been done without offering any specific recommendations. Therefore, Ellet's essay became the first comprehensive study of flood control on the Mississippi. Both reports were sent to Congress in January 1852. What distinguished Ellet's submission was the author's insistence on both the practicability and value of build-

47

Shoring up a levee near Memphis, 1927.

The Corps of Engineers: Dam Destroyers?

On January 15, 1907, Major William Sibert, Pittsburgh district engineer, learned the depressing news that heavy flooding was undermining the abutment of Allegheny River Dam 3. If the dam continued to hold, which seemed likely, the flooding would gradually undermine the bank, thereby threatening a railroad track and a million dollar glass factory. Already nine homes, various outbuildings, and 5.3 acres of land had caved into the river. After long and undoubtedly agonizing discussion with his staff, Major Sibert made his decision: the dam would have to go. To allow the water to continue around the dam was to invite further catastrophe. The next morning blasting began. Five-hundred-pound dynamite charges were placed along the dam crest, and dynamiting continued until a 560-foot section at midstream had been removed. Then stones were placed along the bank to protect the glass factory and the railroad.

On January 30, the *New York Sun* printed an editorial which attacked the lack of progress on waterway projects. However, the editors noted, "no charge of dilatoriness can be brought against the officer who a few weeks ago saved a million dollars worth of property by assuming the responsibility of blowing up $80,000 worth of dam." Sibert became perhaps the only Corps officer ever commended by the Chief of Engineers for blowing up a government dam. His courage, imagination and ability to bend to circumstances set high standards for his successors at the Pittsburgh District Office.

ing reservoirs on the Mississippi's tributaries to reduce flooding. That recommendation prompted Colonel John J. Abert, Chief of the Corps of Topographical Engineers, to write, "While I willingly admit that all the speculations of a man of intellect are full of interest and deserving of careful thought, yet I cannot agree with him that these reservoirs would have any good or preventive effects upon the pernicious inundations of this river . . . ."

Nine years later Humphreys elevated Abert's comment to official Corps policy. After a long convalescence and subsequent work on western railroad surveys, Humphreys took up his task once more in 1857, this time with the assistance of Lieutenant Henry L. Abbot. Abbot supervised a party that took gauge readings, determined discharges at various points, measured cross-sections and reported on the state of various river improvements. When possible, he compared his data with that obtained by earlier survey parties. "In a word," Abbot later wrote, "the finger was to be firmly placed on the pulse of the great river, and every symptom of its annual paroxysm was to be noted." It was in the shadow of the Civil War that Humphreys and Abbot finally put their 500-page report together. They submitted it to the Chief of Topographical Engineers in August 1861, a few months after the firing on Fort Sumter. Humphreys was technically the report's author, but he insisted on listing Abbot as coauthor in recognition of Abbot's diligence and skill.

Humphreys' and Abbot's *Report Upon the Physics and Hydraulics of the Mississippi River* not only contained much new data about the Mississippi, but also analyzed other alluvial rivers around the world. The authors introduced entirely new formulations to explain river flow and sediment resistance and concluded that

Ellet's calculations and assumptions were erroneous. Their own position, based on significantly more information, was that "levees only" could prevent flooding on the Mississippi. Neither reservoirs nor cut-offs were needed. Already a member of the American Philosophical Society, Humphreys received numerous honors for his work on hydraulics. He was made an hono-

Flood at Greenville, Mississippi, 1927.

Flood victims of Arkansas City, Arkansas, camp on a levee, 1927.

The Bicycle Flood Fight, 1897

The Fourth Engineer District at New Orleans received word in early 1897 that a major flood was southbound on the Mississippi. Major George M. Derby, district engineer, and civilian assistant W. J. Hardee prepared to defend the levees along more than 450 miles of river in the Fourth District. As had become customary by 1897, they stationed barges and quarterboats loaded with tools, sandbags and lumber at roughly 15-mile intervals along the river with towboats assigned to each 60-mile section.

During previous flood emergencies, Fourth District personnel had encountered great difficulty maintaining regular patrols of the levee system and coordinating the work of five other agencies: individual planters, railroads, parish governments, levee districts and state government. Backwater and washouts had closed roads and railroads; there then were no motorized vehicles available, and the towboats moved too slowly and usually too far from the levees for proper inspection. In order to improve coordination and inspection, Hardee equipped field personnel with bicycles, and during the subsequent flood fight the inspectors kept constantly on the move atop the levee crowns on their new transportation equipment. Hardee personally covered as much as 30 miles of levee a day on his bike, including stops for observation (and presumably to catch his breath).

High water at Pine Bluff, Arkansas, 1927.

rary member of the Imperial Royal Geological Institute of Vienna in 1862 and a fellow of the American Academy of Arts and Sciences in 1863. The following year he was elected an honorary member of the Royal Institute of Science and Arts of Lombardy, and in 1868 Harvard College conferred upon him the degree of Doctor of Laws.

In considering navigation and flood control as interrelated problems Humphreys, Abbot, Ellet and other engineers in the United States and many in Europe were ahead of their time. By 1879 growing pressures for navigation improvements and flood control prompted Congress to establish the Mississippi River Commission—a seven-member organization responsible for executing a comprehensive plan for flood control and navigation works on the lower Mississippi. This permanent body of experts included three members from the Corps of Engineers, one from the Coast and Geodetic Survey, and three civilians, two of whom had to be civil engineers. The creation of this river basin authority marked the federal government's growing commitment to the development of a reliable inland waterway system. Initially, Congress authorized the commission to build and repair levees only

Carbide lamps illuminate
sandbagging operations on
Mississippi ring levee,
1944.

if the work was part of a general navigation improvement plan. Monumental floods in 1912 and 1913, however, drew national attention to the need for federal flood relief legislation. Finally, in 1917 Congress passed the first flood control act. This legislation appropriated $45 million for flood control on the lower Mississippi and $5.6 million for work on the Sacramento River.

The report of Humphreys and Abbot enormously influenced river engineering in the United States. Until 1927, when a catastrophic flood hit the lower Mississippi, the Corps' position was that "levees only" could control flooding on the river. The Corps was not unalterably opposed to reservoirs. Several were built on the upper Mississippi,

but principally to aid navigation. Advocates of reservoir construction also received support in 1897 from Captain Hiram S. Chittenden of the Corps of Engineers. Chittenden's essay, *Preliminary Examination of Reservoir Sites in Wyoming and Colorado*, submitted in response to a congressional directive, was a comprehensive and lucid presentation of engineering, physiographic and economic data. In it Chittenden declared that reservoir construction in the arid regions of the West was "an indispensable condition to the highest development of that section." He also warned, "The function of reservoirs will always be primarily the promotion of industrial ends; secondarily only, a possible amelioration of flood conditions

in the rivers." So far as the Mississippi was concerned, "the difficulty was not so much a physical as a financial one." He identified a few potential reservoir sites in the Mississippi basin, but thought that flood control alone would never justify construction. He also examined the various methods of constructing reservoirs, noting that the arched dam, first constructed in France in the 1860s, showed promise for use in the West. Finally Chittenden boldly proposed that public agencies, mainly federal, be charged with the responsibility for reservoir development.

With the passage of the second major flood control act in 1928, the federal government became firmly committed to flood control on the Mississippi. This act resulted from the public response to the flooding the year before, which had taken between 250 and 500 lives in the lower Mississippi basin, had flooded more than 16 million acres and had left over half a million people requiring temporary shelter. Two reports were submitted to Congress recommending ways to prevent future disasters of this magnitude, one by the Mississippi River Commission and the other by the Chief of Engineers, Major General Edgar Jadwin. Principally because Jadwin promised equal protection for less than half the money, Congress accepted his plan. This time there was no dispute about levees. The 1927 flood demonstrated the bankruptcy of the "levees only" policy. In addition to levees, Jadwin proposed a mix of floodways and spillways, including the much discussed Bonnet Carré spillway connecting the Mississippi with Lake Pontchartrain. Also included in the plan was the controversial idea of sending about half of the Mississippi's flood waters down the Atchafalaya River into the Gulf of Mexico. This was an idea which Humphreys and Abbot had deemed

Floodwater over Bonnet
Carré spillway.

Sandbagging.

The Benefits of Military Training:
Colonel Eugene Reybold and the
1937 Flood
  During the 1937 floods on the
Ohio and Mississippi Rivers, Lt.
Col. Eugene Reybold, district engineer at Memphis, used his
military expertise to combat the
record high waters. Reybold's
district embraced the Mississippi
and its tributaries from Cairo, Illinois, to the mouth of the Arkansas River. In January, rain equal
to half the normal annual precipi-
tation fell on the Ohio Valley,
causing record floods at every
point on the Ohio River and
sending raging waters rushing
down the Mississippi. The ground
was frozen and the runoff rapid.
The waters threatened Cairo and
the valley below.
  Reybold drew upon his training
at the Command and General
Staff School and the War College
to deal with the situation. He
wrote an estimate of the emergency and organized a defensive
position against the unpredictable
and treacherous enemy. He
called upon the St. Louis and
Kansas City districts for boats
equipped with radios and drew
experienced flood fighters from
all districts. The commanding
general of the 4th Corps Area in
Atlanta supplemented the floating
radio network with Army Signal
Corps units equipped with field
radios and telephones. Reybold
had communications available for
practically every mile of main
levee in his district. Finally, he
set up Red Cross Headquarters
in Memphis to take care of the
anticipated flood refugees.
  From his command post in the
district office in Memphis,
Reybold directed his forces
against the approaching enemy.
There were many dark moments,
but Reybold promptly learned of
each and every weakness in the
levees and quickly had them reinforced. "My military training," he
later observed, "and similar training of countless engineer officers
sent to my assistance had a lot
to do with the safe passage of
the greatest flood the lower Mississippi Valley ever experienced."

"virtually impracticable," but the
Atchafalaya had greatly enlarged
over the years so that most engineers now considered the proposal
workable. On the other hand, Jadwin stood firmly in the tradition of
his predecessor in his opposition to
reservoirs. He had established a
special Reservoir Board of engineer
officers to examine the subject and
the board had concluded that Jadwin's plan was "far cheaper than
any method the board has been able
to devise for accomplishing the
same result by any combination of
reservoirs."
  Nevertheless, the idea of locat-
ing reservoirs on the lower Mississippi was far from dead. In fact, the
Corps' own work stimulated interest in the subject. In 1927 Congress
authorized the Corps to survey the
country's navigable streams in
order to formulate plans for the
improvement of navigation, water
power, flood control, and irrigation.
The surveys came to be called "308
reports," named after Congressional
Document 308 in which the Corps
and the Federal Power Commission
had jointly presented to Congress
the estimated cost for the reports.
Soon after funds were appropriated,
Corps district offices around the
country proceeded with the surveys.
Having dispensed with the main
stem of the Mississippi in the Jadwin plan, district engineers along
the lower Mississippi directed their
attention to the major tributaries.
Not surprisingly, they concluded
that construction of reservoirs
along such streams as the Yazoo
and St. Francis, while contributing
to local flood control, would not be
cost effective. This position proved
increasingly politically unpopular in
the midst of growing unemploy-
ment resulting from the Great
Depression. Public works projects,
once considered uneconomical,
began looking very attractive as a
means of employment. Moreover,
many politicians felt that flood con-

trol was essential to protect human
life no matter what the economists
said. Mainly reacting to this political interest, the Corps reversed its
position on a number of flood control projects. Revised reports
concluded that the necessity for
"public-work relief" and the suffering caused by recurring floods provided grounds for construction.
  The 1936 Flood Control Act
recognized that flood control was "a
proper activity of the Federal Government in cooperation with States,
their political subdivisions, and
localities thereof." Responsibility
for federal flood control projects
was given to the Corps of Engineers, while projects dealing with
watershed run-off and soil erosion
were assigned to the Department of
Agriculture. This law made the
Corps responsible for flood control
throughout the nation, working in
cooperation with the Bureau of
Reclamation. In the years following
passage of this law, the Corps built,
pursuant to congressional authorization and appropriation, some
300-400 reservoirs whose primary
benefit was flood control. However,
it is inconceivable that these reservoirs would have been built had
flood control been the only benefit.
In the age of multipurpose projects,
possible navigation, water storage,
irrigation, power and recreation
benefits were considered before a
final economic benefit figure was
determined.

Hydropower Development

Office of History, Corps of Engineers

Brigadier General
Alexander Mackenzie.

Libby Dam, Montana.

Public Affairs Office, Corps of Engineers

Public Affairs Office, Corps of Engineers

Generators at Bonneville
Dam.

Since the turn of the 20th century, the U.S. Army Corps of Engineers has moved from a position opposing involvement in hydroelectric power to one of total endorsement. By 1900 Congress had already initiated partial federal control over dam-building. The Corps participated in the regulatory process but conceived its role narrowly.

In January 1905 Brigadier General Alexander Mackenzie, the Chief of Engineers, summed up the Corps' traditional views on the federal government's limited role in improving American waterways. Congress, he said, could legally "exercise control over the navigable waters of the United States . . . only to the extent necessary to protect, preserve, and improve free naviga-

tion." Mackenzie further maintained that nothing should be permitted to interfere with the central purpose of locks and dams—to facilitate navigation and commerce. All other interests were clearly secondary. These views fitted into the prevailing judicial interpretation of federal powers under the Constitution's commerce clause.

During the years following Mackenzie's pronouncements, attitudes gradually changed. The engineers became convinced that the escalation in private dam-building, largely for hydropower purposes, threatened to jeopardize their prerogatives in navigation work and they guarded those prerogatives jealously. While the federal government redefined its part in water

John Day Lock and Dam.

resources development, the Corps staked out its own territory. As an auxiliary to navigation and later to flood control, hydropower benefited by more liberal interpretations of federal authority. Cautiously, with frequent hesitation and some inconsistency, the engineers embraced the new philosophy. What began as a regulatory role in hydropower expanded to include much more. By mid-century, the Corps of Engineers emerged as the largest constructor and operator of federal power facilities.

The change in the engineers' role was dramatic by the end of the 1920s. By that time, they were heavily involved in surveying rivers for flood control, power and irrigation, as well as for navigation. Public power at multipurpose projects took hold during the New Deal and proliferated after World War II. In the mid-1950s, the Corps had more than 20 multipurpose projects under construction. By 1975 the energy produced by Corps hydroelectric facilities was 27 percent of the total hydroelectric power production in the United States and 4.4 percent of the electrical energy output from all sources. In 1987 the Corps was operating and maintaining 73 projects with hydropower facilities. The total capacity at Corps dams was about 20.1 million kilowatts. The largest hydropower dams built by the Corps are on the Columbia and Snake rivers in the Pacific Northwest. The biggest of these is the John Day on the Columbia River, which has a generating capacity of nearly 2.2 million kilowatts.

In 1951 the Chief of Engineers referred to the development of hydropower as "one of the most important aspects of water resource development." Further, he argued, "proper provisions for hydroelectric power development are an essential part of comprehensive planning for conservation and use of our river basins for the greatest public good." Nearly 20 years later, the Office of the Chief of Engineers reaffirmed its commitment, stating that "generation of hydroelectric power to serve the growing needs of the American people is a task the Corps welcomes." The Corps' turnabout and its expanding mission in hydroelectric power development were a significant part of the organization's history in the first six decades of the 20th century. Today, the Corps continues to operate, maintain, and occasionally add capacity at existing hydroelectric plants.

Clark Hill Lake and Dam,
Savannah River, Georgia and
South Carolina.

Fort Peck Spillway, Montana.

Power house turbine blade under repair.

Bonneville Dam on the Columbia River, Oregon and Washington.

Powerhouse construction, Richard B. Russell Dam on the Savannah River, 1982.

The Environmental Challenge

Mirror Lake, Yellowstone, 1880.

Public Affairs Office, Corps of Engineers

Office of History, Corps of Engineers

Original Baronett Bridge, first across the Yellowstone River, built in 1871.

Buffalo grazing at Yellowstone, 1880.

As explorers and mapmakers for the pioneers, the engineers were among the first to recognize the need for protection of natural resources. As early as the 1840s, when the vast herds of buffalo seemed limitless to most travelers, engineer officers warned of their impending destruction. Captain Howard Stansbury noted their shrinking ranges and warned that the buffalo "seem destined to final extirpation at the hands of men." These officers were nearly correct, but one of the few surviving buffalo herds today is protected at a Corps of Engineers project.

The Corps of Engineers was also influential in the creation of the first national park at Yellowstone in 1874, and the Corps operated and protected that park for many years. Captain William Ludlow and an engineer survey party at Yellowstone in the 1870s confronted tourists, harbingers of the future, carving their initials, scattering their rubbish and breaking off pieces of rock formations. Alarmed, Ludlow pleaded with the visitors to respect nature's work. He stopped one woman, poised with a shovel over a mound formed over thousands of years by a bubbling spring's mineral deposits, in time to prevent her smashing the formation. In his report, Ludlow proposed several ways to protect the new park. His recommendations, including military patrols and engineer construction of roads, were adopted. Thanks to Ludlow, who provided the blueprint for saving the park, Yellowstone remains among the crown jewels of America's scenic wonders.

To prevent the obstruction of navigable waterways, Congress in the 1870s directed the Corps to regulate the construction of specific bridges. The job was expanded during the 1880s and '90s to prevent dumping and filling in the nation's harbors, a program that was vigorously enforced by the engineers. At the port of Pittsburgh in 1892, for instance, the Corps took a grand jury on a boat tour of the harbor and obtained some 50 indictments of firms dumping debris into the harbor. When the engineers learned that firms were piling debris on the streambanks during the day and pushing it into the harbor at night,

57

Assessing a "sea curtain" for containing oil spills.

Public Affairs Office, Corps of Engineers

they began night patrols in fast boats with searchlights.

In 1893 a citizen of an Ohio River city complained to the Corps that the city was dumping into the river "household garbage, refuse of wholesale commission and slaughter houses, wagon loads of decaying melons, fruit and vegetables and carcasses of animals." The city officials replied that the complaint was exaggerated—very few dead animals were dumped in the river—and refused to stop the practice because the city then would have to build incinerators to dispose of the refuse. The Corps managed to stop the dumping anyway, forced the city to build an incinerator and prosecuted the offenders, arguing that the garbage formed piles sufficient to obstruct navigation.

In the Rivers and Harbors Act of 1899, Congress gave the Corps the authority to regulate almost all kinds of obstructions to navigation. The engineers were disappointed that they were not also given authority to deal with polluters, for many of their personnel lived on the waterways on a daily basis and

water quality was an immediate personal concern.

The Corps used the Rivers and Harbors Act of 1899 to the fullest extent legally possible to protect the environment of navigable waterways. In one extreme instance the Corps managed to stop a firm from discharging a liquid effluent into a waterway by contending in court that the discharge obstructed navigation because it entered steamboat boilers and corroded them to the extent that repairs were necessary. The Oil Pollution Act of 1924 gave the Corps the responsibility of insuring that offensive and dangerous oil discharges did not pollute the nation's harbors. However, the Corps could not adequately control the problem because of lack of regulatory power and insufficient manpower, and Corps officers periodically urged Congress to grant the agency adequate authority and resources.

The Corps' regulatory authority was expanded by the Clean Water Act (Federal Water Pollution Control Act) of 1972 to include all waters of the United States. The Corps began to regulate discharges

of dredged or fill materials into any waters of the United States and the permit program that resulted gave environmental protection the fullest consideration. "We would like to commend the Corps for the will with which it is turning to carrying out the responsibilities Congress gave it in Section 404 for protecting the water quality on which the health and economic well-being of every American depend," said a member of the Natural Resources Defense Council.

Along with protective measures for the environment, the Corps at its authorized projects pursues an active program for the preservation of cultural resources. Recent legislation stipulates that up to one percent of the funds for a project can be expended for cultural resource surveys, for artifact and data recovery, and for mitigation efforts. The Corps' cultural resource preservation effort has had substantial results. For example, the Corps relocated a navigation lock on the Tennessee-Tombigbee Waterway to avoid destroying an Indian burial ground; and in Pennsylvania the Corps moved a unique 19th-century wagon works from a project area to preserve it. To avoid accidental destruction of archeological sites, the Corps is searching for the homes of ancient tribes, especially along the coasts where dredge disposal sites are needed.

The Corps' responsibility for improving and maintaining navigation on the nation's waterways requires the dredging of channels if they are to remain open. In 1969 the dredging program was attacked as environmentally unsound. "All of a sudden, dredging became a four-letter word," remarked Lieutenant General John Morris of the Corps. "Now this came as rather a surprise to us," he continued, "since dredging has been a daily activity within the Corps for 150 years and nobody paid much attention to it."

Restored Gruber Wagon Works, Berks County, Pennsylvania

Office of History, Corps of Engineers

The Dalles, Oregon.

Public Affairs Office, Corps of Engineers

In 1970 the Corps began a dredged material research program to identify dredging and dredged disposal systems that would be compatible with the new environmental protection mission. Completed in 1978, the dredged material research program reversed some traditional thinking about the effects of dredging. It indicated that dredging need not have adverse impacts on aquatic life and that dredged materials can create new wetlands and wildlife management areas. The research identified improved methods for constructing diked disposal areas and for using physical, chemical and biological agents in the dredging process and it demonstrated that dredged fill can be used to reclaim strip-mined lands and other environmentally damaged areas.

Streambank erosion can have major detrimental impacts on the environment and human welfare. It results in sediment deposits in reservoirs and waterways; it impairs navigation, flood control and water supply project effectiveness; it blights valuable recreation areas and streambank lands. Since 1969 the Corps has conducted intensive studies of streambank erosion, with demonstration control projects along the Missouri, Ohio and Yazoo rivers, in an effort to identify the causes of such erosion and to find new techniques for bank protection. The studies of this form of environmental degradation have identified the causes of streambank erosion and have indicated some potential new techniques for its control.

The Corps' coastal engineering research program since 1969 has devised some innovative approaches to the problems of beach erosion, coastal storm damages and navigation along the coastline. Analysis of wave patterns has opened the way to rational design of rubble mound structures for the protection of threatened beaches and coastline. Possible uses for beach and marsh grasses in control of coastal erosion have been identified. And the research has established some basic relationships governing the size and shape of coastal inlets and harbor entrances.

Fish and wildlife conservation has been a concern of the Corps since Captain Stansbury warned that the buffalo were disappearing. The engineers built the first federal fish hatchery in 1879–1880 and have included such features as fish ladders in project planning for many years. Corps projects are designed to minimize damage to fish and wildlife resources, and the Corps enhances wildlife resources at its projects through effective wildlife management. Approximately 2.5 million acres of land are primarily used for fish and wildlife purposes; one-fifth of this land is managed by other federal and state agencies in cooperation with the Corps.

The intense interest of the Corps in fish and wildlife management derives in part from the program's value to the recreational functions at 463 Corps water resource projects covering an aggregate of more than 11 million acres. Over 400 million visitors annually enjoy fishing, hunting, swimming and other water-related sports at Corps recreation areas.

Through its floodplain management program begun in 1960, the Corps provides technical services and planning guidance for many local agencies and groups to encourage prudent use of floodplains. At the request of local agencies, the Corps studies specific areas to identify flood hazard potentials, to establish standard project floods and flood frequency curves, and to map the floodplains. The resulting information is used by the local agencies to regulate floodplain development, even to the extent of evacuating floodprone areas and converting them to recreation parks or fish and wildlife habitats.

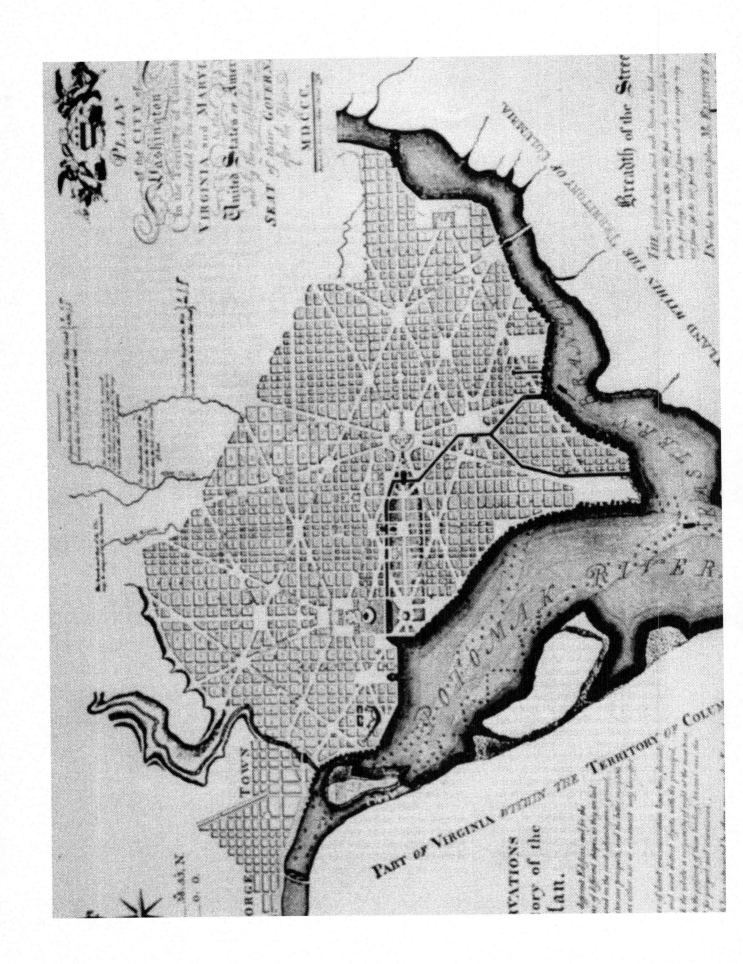

Work in the District of Columbia

Cabin John Bridge.

Office of History, Corps of Engineers

Montgomery C. Meigs.

Andrew Ellicott's plan of Washington, D.C. 1792.

Army engineers contributed to both the planning and construction of the nation's capital. From early bridges to the modern subway system, Corps officers and civilians helped plan and construct Washington's transportation system, city monuments and public buildings. Parks, water supply and sewage systems, flood control structures and public health measures in the city were or still are the engineers' responsibility. Army engineers served as administrators as well as construction experts. Their influence and responsibilities declined only as civilian agencies assumed control of certain activities and home-rule movements lessened federal responsibility for public works in Washington.

In 1791 former Army Engineer Pierre Charles L'Enfant designed the master plan for the new capital. Other Army engineers designed and built fortifications for the city. The British Army destroyed some of those defenses as well as the partially built Capitol building during the War of 1812. Chief Engineer Joseph G. Swift helped rebuild the Capitol. In 1822 Major Isaac Rober-

deau, a topographical engineer, supervised the installation of cast iron pipes to bring spring water to the White House and the executive offices around it. In the 1850s, Congress funded the construction of a permanent water supply for the cities of Washington and Georgetown. Eventually placed under the supervision of engineer First Lieutenant Montgomery C. Meigs, the project evolved into what is today the Washington Aqueduct Office of the U.S. Army Engineer District, Baltimore. Meigs' plans included construction of two bridges to carry traffic as well as water pipes, one over Cabin John Creek and one over Rock Creek. Both bridges were engineering feats of their time and the Cabin John Bridge remains in use. This bridge, begun in 1857 and completed in 1864, held the world's record for 40 years for having the longest masonry arch in the world.

Meigs and other engineer officers also reconstructed the United States Capitol, fireproofed the Smithsonian Institution and rebuilt or repaired bridges and streets. Using new techniques, Meigs provided

61

U.S. Capitol dome,
December 31, 1857.

Interior of the Capitol,
photographed from the
dome.

the first adequate heating and ventilation system for the home of Congress. As construction of the two new wings of the Capitol progressed, the old dome began to look disproportionately small, and a new dome was designed that consisted of cast and wrought iron and weighed almost nine million pounds. President Abraham Lincoln used the completion of that dome during the Civil War as a symbol of his intention to preserve the Union.

After the Civil War, Corps officers and civilians designed and built many of the monuments and public buildings that decorate Washington today. At the request of the Senate, Major Nathaniel Michler surveyed sites for a new park and a new location for the White House. His praise drew attention to Rock Creek Valley. Later, the Chief of Engineers, Brigadier General Thomas L. Casey, and other officers worked for and supervised the development of that large urban park.

Congress continued to institutionalize the Corps' role in the District. In 1867 the legislators removed control of many public buildings from civilian hands and gave it to what became the Office of Public Buildings and Grounds under the Chief of Engineers. In 1878 Congress permanently replaced Washington's elected government with a three-man commission. An Army engineer holding the title of Engineer Commissioner for the District of Columbia served on that governing board with responsibility for the city's physical plant. Meanwhile, other engineer work in the District grew to the extent that the Chief of Engineers, Brigadier General Andrew A. Humphreys, established in 1874 the United States Engineer Office, Washington, under the civilian engineer Sylvanus T. Abert, to carry out navigation improvements on the Potomac River and its tributaries.

Thomas L. Casey prepares to set aluminum apex for Washington Monument, from a sketch made for *Harper's Weekly*.

Library of Congress under construction, 1888.

Daniel Chester French's Abraham Lincoln, Lincoln Memorial, Washington, D.C.

Two years later, Congress asked the Corps to complete the Washington Monument, left partially built by its bankrupt sponsors. Then Lieutenant Colonel Thomas Casey and his assistant, Bernard Green, corrected major problems with its foundation, redesigned it and supervised its completion. The construction culminated in December 1884, with the placing on its tip of a pyramid of 100 ounces of aluminum, the largest piece yet cast in the Western Hemisphere of the new metal. Casey and Green went on to help design and supervise the construction of the State, War and Navy Building next to the White House. It is now the Executive Office Building. The two men also helped design and construct the Library of Congress.

Between the 1880s and the 1920s, Corps dredge and fill operations not only protected Washington from Potomac and Anacostia river floods, but also created waterfront park land. Potomac Park, Washington Channel with its adjacent recreation areas and the land for the Lincoln and Jefferson memorials all are products of this river improvement and swamp reclamation work. The attractive tidal basin in front of the Jefferson memorial that automatically changes the water in the Washington Channel with the tidal flow is another product of this work.

Meanwhile Lieutenant Colonel William W. Harts of the Office of Buildings and Grounds took charge of the development of Rock Creek Park, which became a major resource for urban recreation and beauty. Harts also supervised the completion of three important memorials. In 1913 he directed the start of work on the new headquarters of the American Red Cross. The following year he oversaw the beginning of construction on the Lincoln Memorial and the Arlington

Memorial Amphitheater and Chapel.

The Corps also built or supervised the construction of practical and attractive buildings to house the government of the reunited nation, including the Government Printing Office and the Army War College at Fort McNair. In 1883 Meigs came out of retirement to build the Pension Building. Designed to house the offices providing pensions to war veterans, the building is so attractive that it is sometimes used for inaugural activities.

The George Washington Memorial Parkway, the Pentagon and National Airport began as pre-World War II construction projects of the Corps of Engineers. After World War II, the Corps was involved in the complete gutting and rebuilding of the inside of the White House, expanding the water supply for the District and planning for housing and transportation.

U. S. Grant III, grandson of the President, and other officers served on the planning boards that oversaw growth in the Washington metropolitan area. Gradually, civilian agencies such as the National Park Service began to assume responsibility for developing the buildings, streets, sewage systems and parks which the Corps had handled in addition to its ordinary activities.

The Washington Aqueduct alone remains a special responsibility of the U.S. Army Engineer District, Baltimore. The Baltimore District also carries out all current civil works and military projects in the Washington area, including the massive renovation project for the Pentagon.

Washington Monument, February 1884.

PLAN

of

FORT WASHINGTON

U. STATES

Coast Defense

Plan for drawbridge and portcullis at Fort Pulaski, c.1846.

Civil War soldiers at Castle Pinckney, Charleston Harbor.

Massachusetts Commandery Military Order of the Loyal Legion

Plan of Fort Washington, November 1823.

When the American Revolution began in 1775, numerous coastal fortifications already existed along the Atlantic coast to protect communities from pirate incursions and enemy raids. The British Royal Engineers, as well as individual colonies and local communities, built these structures, which varied from crude earthen and wooden batteries to strong masonry forts.

During the War for Independence, the combatants rehabilitated many of the existing coastal fortifications and constructed new ones. The small body of Continental Army Engineers accomplished some of the work. Then, when the war ended, the new country abandoned these works, deciding that the militia could man them, if necessary.

A decade later, in 1794, the United States, fearing attacks from other nations, undertook a construction program to provide fortifications for the protection of the major harbors and northern frontiers of the country. Until the 1860s, the Corps of Engineers planned and erected these works, which were often elaborate structures. Initially the Corps followed the prevalent French and British designs, but later developed its own, more modern ones. Fort Monroe in Virginia, Fort Adams in Rhode Island and Fort Washington in Maryland exhibit foreign influence while Fort Delaware, Delaware, and Fort Point, California, reflect American concepts.

Interior of Fort
Independence, Boston
Harbor, 1864.

Bombardment of Fort
McHenry, aquatint by John
Bower, undated.

Plan of Fort Sumter, Charleston
Harbor, c. 1828.

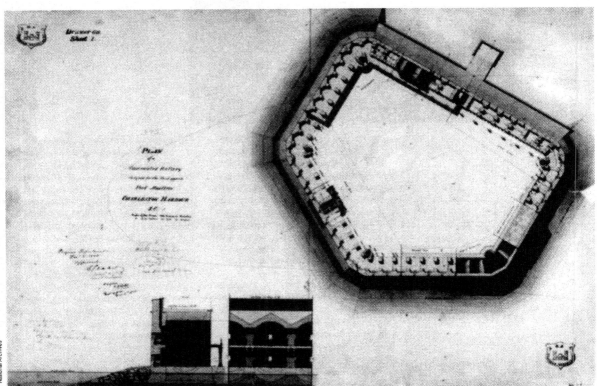

Inspection at Fort Monroe, Virginia, c.1900.

Diagram of torpedo used in the War of 1812, from Benson J. Lossing's *The Pictorial Field Book of the War of 1812.*

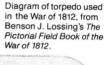

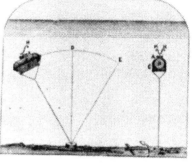

Although generally ungarrisoned, the country's coastal fortifications were a viable deterrent to foreign attack until the Civil War, when newly developed weapons rendered these defenses obsolete. Heavy rifled artillery, both land and naval, demolished brick, stone and masonry fortifications like Fort Sumter, South Carolina, and Fort Pulaski, Georgia. As a result, both Union and Confederate engineers began erecting coastal forts and batteries that were much more resilient to artillery fire.

Forsaking the outdated coastal fortifications, the engineers, acting upon a coast defense board's recommendations, began building concrete gun batteries to defend the coasts of the United States. Theoretically, long-range guns and mortars in these batteries would destroy enemy fleets before they reached a harbor. The Army engineers sometimes placed the batteries inside or in the immediate vicinity of old coastal forts. They purchased new land for others and with the acquisition of new territories at the end of the century, began erecting batteries in Hawaii, Panama and the Philippines. As artillery improved, the Corps constructed new batteries for bigger and more efficient guns.

Later, after World War II, new weapons like the airplane and missile rendered the batteries obsolete. By 1950 the Army ceased using them for their original purpose. Today the remnants of these batteries dot the coast and often appear from a distance to look like concrete bunkers.

In conjunction with its fortification and battery construction programs, Army engineers had other coast defense responsibilities. In the 19th century, they placed obstructions in the bays, rivers and harbors along the coasts. Progressing from chains to submarine mines, these obstructions were to slow down or halt enemy vessels. Although the Coast Artillery Corps took over responsibility for submarine mines in 1901, the Corps continued to build casemates, storehouses, loading rooms and other structures for the mine defenses. The Corps also developed a protective concealment program for coast defenses evolving into the elaborate camouflage nets and paints in use during World War II.

Fort Sumter before the Civil War, from an oil painting by Seth Eastman.

Combat Operations

**from the Mexican War
to the Mexican Punitive
Expedition**

Union troops at gun
emplacement, 1863

The Mexican War

On May 15, 1846, soon after the Mexican War began, Congress authorized the War Department to raise a company of engineers. This unit, the first regular Army engineer company, acted as sappers and miners during the arduous and lengthy marches of the war. It also erected siege batteries at Mexico City, an important contribution to the assault of that capital.

At the Battle of Contreras in August 1847, Lieutenant Gustavus W. Smith, then commanding the engineer company, asked for and received permission to participate in the attack. Smith and his men initially led the assault, which the commanding general halted and rescheduled for the next morning upon observing the arrival of enemy reinforcements. The next morning, the engineer company, along with a rifle regiment, attacked the Mexicans in the rear. Most of the enemy troops fled, but a few remained to fire grapeshot at the Americans from about 25 yards. Although partially shaken by the blast, the engineer company chased the fleeing Mexicans for some distance before receiving orders to return to the main army.

In all 44 engineer officers served in the Mexican War including Robert E. Lee, George B. McClellan, P.G.T. Beauregard and Henry W. Halleck. Practically all of these engineers served on the staffs of general officers and performed reconnaissance and intelligence

work, especially around Mexico City.

Following the Mexican War, the engineer officers returned to peacetime duties, including fortification construction, exploration, surveying and river, harbor and road work. The engineer company, which spent a good deal of its time at West Point in the postwar period, did accompany some exploring expeditions to the West and performed other tasks in various parts of the country. Although the Army fought many Indian Wars during this period, the engineers were seldom involved.

The Civil War

Thirteen years after the Mexican War, the Civil War erupted. For Civil War service, the War Department increased the number of regular Army engineer troops to four companies, constituting one battalion. This battalion, along with the various volunteer engineer and pioneer units, cleared obstacles; constructed roads, bridges, palisades, stockades, canals, blockhouses, signal towers and in one instance, a church; laid down hundreds of ponton bridges; and erected field fortifications, augmenting them with entanglements. Often, these units accomplished their work under extremely adverse conditions. At Fredericksburg, Virginia, in December 1862, they laid six ponton bridges across the Rappahannock River under devastating fire from Confederate sharpshooters. In June 1864, Army of the

Major General Gustavus W.
Smith (Civil War-era photo).

Ponton bridge.

Parrott guns in Number 1
Battery near Yorktown, May
1862.

Potomac engineer troops constructed a 2,170-foot ponton bridge across the James River, the longest floating bridge ever constructed by U.S. Army Engineers.

When the Civil War began, two engineer corps existed in the Union Army, the Topographical Engineers and the Engineers. But the exigencies of the war required stricter coordination of engineer activities. Therefore in 1863, the War Department integrated the smaller Corps of Topographical Engineers into the Corps of Engineers under the command of the Chief Engineer. The title changed to Chief of Engineers in 1866.

The Union Engineers could not benefit from the talents of McClellan, Halleck, George G. Meade, William S. Rosecrans, William B. Franklin, Gouverneur K. Warren, James B. McPherson and Andrew A. Humphreys, who all became general officers commanding combined troops. Likewise, Montgomery C. Meigs was the quartermaster general of the Union Army and furnished the required support and supplies to the troops in the field. By the end of the war, James H. Wilson was a cavalry general.

Other able officers though, like Henry Brewerton, John G. Barnard and Nathaniel Michler, were engineers throughout the war. These men conducted surveys and reconnaissances to provide useful intelligence reports and maps; directed siege operations; and oversaw the operations of engineer troops. Three young engineer lieutenants, William H. H. Benyaurd, John M. Wilson and George L. Gillespie, received Congressional Medals of Honor for gallantry under fire and the latter two concluded their Army careers as Chief of Engineers. Competent volunteer engineer officers like William G. Margedant, who developed a process for duplicating maps in the field, also greatly aided the Union war effort.

The Confederacy gladly accepted the services of 15 engineer officers who resigned their commissions in the U.S. Army. Former engineer officers, such as Lee, Beauregard and Joseph E. Johnston, became Confederate army commanders. Edward P. Alexander was the Confederate artillery commander in the Army of Northern Virginia. To accomplish the necessary engineer work, the Confederacy commissioned many former civilians and raised engineer and pioneer units.

Ponton bridge across the
Rappahannock River, built
by the 50th and 15th New
York Engineers, 1863.

U.S. Army engineers
building a military railroad,
1862.

70

Remodeled Confederate
fort, part of federal line
of defenses for Atlanta,
November 1864.

Troops at Fort Wagner
bombproof.

Railroad trestle bridge built by
1st Michigan Engineers and
Mechanics Regiment at
Whiteside, Tennessee, in 1864.
The four-tiered bridge was 780
feet long.

**The Use of Civil Experience in
Wartime: Gouverneur K. Warren
at Gettysburg**

By the summer of 1863, Major
General Gouverneur K. Warren,
United States Volunteers, had
developed a keen eye for terrain.
As a Topographical Engineer during the 1850s, Warren had led
three exploring expeditions into
Nebraska and the Dakotas. In addition he had produced the first
comprehensive map of the trans-
Mississippi West, an accomplishment that has brought him wide
and deserved acclaim.

This talent for assessing terrain, nurtured in civil assignments
before the secession crisis, stood
Warren in good stead during the
Civil War. On the second day of
the battle of Gettysburg, Warren
saw that the hill called Little
Round Top on the southern flank
of the Union line was weakly defended. Right away he knew that
a strong Confederate attack on
the hill menaced the entire Army.
To the west, on Seminary Ridge,
Confederate General John B.
Hood reached the same conclusion and sent a force to take the
hill. When Hood's men arrived
they found strong Union reinforcements already in place. After
a sharp fight, the Confederates
withdrew. Warren had beaten
them to the hill and saved the
day for the Union.

Students at Willets Point
building a ponton bridge,
1889.

Post-Civil War Period

After the Civil War and until the outbreak of the Spanish American War, engineer combat experience was minimal. Most engineer officers returned to civil works or fortification construction duty. Nevertheless, engineers attempted to stay abreast of new military engineering methods and innovations.

Soon after the Civil War ended, Congress abolished the Corps of Engineers' supervision of the U.S. Military Academy at West Point, New York. Therefore the Corps, unofficially at first, established an Engineer School at Fort Totten, Willets Point, New York Harbor, in 1866. The school's staff instructed the students, both officers and enlisted men, in civil and military engineering and provided practical training in mapping, military photography and laying submarine mines and bridges, both ponton and trestle. Besides teaching, the staff, especially Henry L. Abbot, who was the superintendent, experimented with and developed new equipment.

Some officers did serve with the "Indian-fighting army" on the western frontier. A few, like William Ludlow, accompanied the troops on reconnaissances and scouting expeditions. Generally though, these officers' main duties were surveying and mapping.

Other officers such as Barton S. Alexander, Cyrus B. Comstock, Peter S. Michie, John M. Wilson, William Craighill, William E. Merrill and William Ludlow travelled abroad, sometimes as military attaches. Often, they had the chance to observe foreign engineer troops, equipment and techniques. A few, including Francis V. Greene, actually witnessed engineer operations in battle.

The War Department created a fifth regular army company of engineers in December 1865. Between the Civil War and the Spanish American War the five companies of the battalion, usually under-strength, performed various duties from serving at engineer depots in New York Harbor, St. Louis and San Francisco to riot control during the 1877 railroad strikes. Individual engineer soldiers assisted at numerous civil works and fortification sites throughout the country.

Underwater mine testing at
the Engineer School, Willets
Point, New York.

We Don't Surrender Much!

At the end of 1862 Colonel William D. Innes and 391 men of the First Michigan Engineers were repairing roads and railroads at the rear of the Union Army near Murfreesboro (Stone's River), Tennessee, when a Confederate cavalry division commanded by General Joseph Wheeler flanked the Union Army to strike hard at supply trains on the way from Nashville to Stone's River. The surprise attack left Innes and the engineers without time to escape the gray-clad troopers, and Innes rushed his unit up a nearby hill.

From the top of the hill Innes could see the advancing Confederate columns and realized he had no time to entrench his position. But the hill was covered with clumps of red cedar trees and Innes quickly decided to use this resource. He sent the engineers scrambling around the hill, slashing down the small trees to open a field of fire and piling the cedars in a waist-high circle around the crest of the hill.

Confederates in greatly superior force soon surrounded the hill. An officer under a flag of truce advanced to demand surrender from the engineer detachment and was surprised by Innes's acerbic reply: "Tell General Wheeler I'll see him damned first." Innes continued, "We don't surrender much. Let him take us."

Confederate cavalry soldiers swept up the hill toward the position, but a volley of union fire hurled them back pell-mell. The Confederates then unlimbered field artillery and began pounding the hill, but the engineers scraped shallow foxholes and held their place. A second cavalry assault followed and then a third. In all the cavalry made seven attempts to take the hill, yet the engineers stood their ground until the Confederates concluded the effort was not worth the cost. The engineers suffered 11 casualties; the Confederates nearly 50.

Engineers' train in the Philippines during the Insurrection.

Guards at trenches dug by engineers, Guantanamo, Cuba.

The Spanish-American War and Philippine Insurrection

In 1898 the United States went to war with Spain and the engineers provided extensive combat support. In the far-flung theaters of the war from Cuba and Puerto Rico to the Philippines, the engineers aided the Army by erecting landing piers, constructing bridges, building and maintaining roads and repairing and operating railroads. Young but capable lieutenants, like Lytle Brown, Eben E. Winslow and William D. Connor, led engineer detachments on dangerous reconnaissance missions, sometimes in the midst of combat. Volunteer engineer units, often commanded by regular army officers, also served in the war. Former engineer officers, such as Francis V. Greene and William Ludlow, were brigade and higher unit commanders.

Following the Spanish-American War, an insurrection broke out in the Philippines. Companies A and B of the Engineer Battalion served in the initial stages of the conflict. The insurrectionists' guerrilla warfare tactics necessitated rapid Army movements. Thus, engineer detachments, commanded by William Sibert, John Biddle, John C. Oakes and Harley B. Ferguson, among others, had to repair roads, build bridges and perform reconnaissance rapidly over difficult jungle and mountain terrain. Frequently the engineer troops, who carried rifles as well as picks and axes, joined the infantry in fighting off an attack before completing work on a road or bridge. The requirements of combat, especially in the Philippines, influenced the 1901 reorganization of the engineers into three battalions of four companies each. Although the fighting subsided in the Philippines in the early 20th century, it did not cease, and engineer troops served in the islands, often in combat, for many years afterwards.

The Mexican Punitive Expedition

In 1916 the Corps of Engineers formed three regiments of six companies each from the battalions. In the same year, the United States launched a punitive expedition to Mexico to chastise the "bandits" under Pancho Villa who had raided American Territory. The use of cars and supply trucks required better roads and bridges than ever before. Lytle Brown, now a major, was only one of many engineer officers who served in Mexico. Most likely, these officers were thankful for the experience which was put to the test after April 1917, when the United States entered World War I.

Postcard showing troops near the Mexican border.

The Panama Canal

Drilling on Contractor's Hill at Culebra Cut, January 1912.

Culebra Cut.

West chamber of Gatun Upper Locks, March 1912.

In the early morning of May 4, 1904, a young second lieutenant crisply walked into the old French hotel in Panama City. He exchanged brief greetings with officials of the new French Panama Canal Company. The company, which had succeeded Ferdinand de Lesseps' bankrupt enterprise in 1894, had been no more successful than its predecessor in its effort to build a canal across the Isthmus of Panama connecting the Pacific and Atlantic oceans. Its workers ravaged by malaria, its equipment in a state of disrepair, the company was ready to sell all of its assets to the United States government for $40 million. The lieutenant carefully read the document of transfer. Then, following the directions of the American secretary of war, he signed his name to the receipt: "Mark Brooke, 2nd Lieutenant, Corps of Engineers." The French effort was over. The American attempt was about to begin.

Building the Panama Canal required the assistance of the foremost engineers of the day. Major William M. Black, who later became Chief of Engineers, supervised early engineering activities at the canal. John F. Wallace, first civilian chief engineer on the project, brought railroad construction and operations expertise to the Isthmus. His successor, John F. Stevens, continued his endeavors and established the basic plan for the construction of the canal. He resigned, however, in 1907 when he was severely criticized in the United States. Frustrated by his inability to find a civilian willing to see the project through to completion, President Theodore Roosevelt turned for help to the Corps of Engineers. "We can't build the Canal with a new chief engineer every year," he said. "Now I'm going to give it to the Army and to someone who can't quit." He requested the Panama Canal Commission to appoint Engineer officer Lieutenant Colonel George W. Goethals as chief engineer and commission chairman. Engineer officers Major William L. Sibert and Major David D. Gaillard, both West Point graduates like Goethals, also served on the commission. All three men received promotions during the time they worked on the canal.

Pedro Miguel Locks under
construction, January 1911.

Within a year Goethals reorganized canal operations into three geographical divisions. Sibert took charge of the Atlantic Division, and Gaillard took the Central Division. To head the Pacific Division, Goethals selected Sydney B. Williamson, a civilian engineer who had won his respect when the two had worked together earlier at Muscle Shoals. The civilian engineers under Williamson engaged in a spirited competition with the military engineers. Goethals encouraged this competition to achieve maximum economy while speeding construction. Rear Admiral Harry H. Rousseau, Chief of the Bureau of Yards and Docks of the Navy, assumed responsibility for the design and construction of terminals, wharves, docks, warehouses, machine shops and coaling stations. Civilian engineer Ralph Budd directed the relocation of the Panama Railroad from 1907 until 1909, when he was succeeded by Lieutenant Frederick Mears of the Corps of Engineers.

In the 1880s the French had learned after several years of effort that a sea-level canal across Panama was an impossibility. Locks were absolutely necessary. Benefitting from French mistakes, Americans never seriously considered anything other than a canal utilizing locks. They erected a monumental dam across the Chagres River, thereby creating Lake Gatun. At each end of the lake, the engineers constructed locks. The Gatun Locks lead to the Atlantic. The Pedro Miguel Locks lead to Miraflores Lake and, farther on, Miraflores Locks. From these locks ships travel on to the Pacific.

Major Gaillard directed the huge engineering task of completing the Culebra Cut through the continental divide, which required the excavation of 96 million cubic yards of rock and dirt. Spectacular landslides at the Cut were the greatest engineering difficulty. The amount

Work in progress.

Miraflores Lower Locks,
August 1912.

S.S. *Cristobal* in Gatun Upper Locks, August 3, 1914.

U.S. Aircraft Carrier *Saratoga* in Gaillard Cut, February 1928.

Office of History, Corps of Engineers

Goethals Collection.
U.S. Military Academy Library

of earth that had to be removed was nearly double the original estimate. More than 100 steam shovels removed most of the soil, and flatcars hauled it out. Trains departed at 13-minute intervals to keep pace with the steam shovels.

Construction of the Panama Canal was never the responsibility of the Army Corps of Engineers, but having engineer officers supervising the project enabled problems to be resolved easier than before, if not always to everyone's satisfaction. For instance, in 1910 President William Howard Taft dispatched Brigadier General William L. Marshall, then Chief of Engineers, to the Canal Zone when a disagreement arose between Goethals and Sibert over the design for the floor of the upper lock at Gatun. Sibert insisted on a gravity section to resist the upward pressure of the full Gatun Lake level, which would act as a lifting force whenever the upper chamber was unwatered. He also wanted to anchor the floor to foundation rock with bent steel rails left by the French. Goethals believed this an extravagant double precaution. He had promised to construct the canal within cost estimates and was unwilling to authorize the additional work Sibert desired.

While not criticizing Goethals' concern for staying within the budget, Marshall decided that Sibert was right. He recommended to President Taft that the double safety factor be adopted. To make sure that Goethals understood he meant what he said, Marshall told him, "I'm going to advise Mr. Taft to keep you both where you are, BUT if you can't get along together, I'm going to advise his keeping Sibert here and ordering you elsewhere." This apparently cleared the air, and the two engineer officers worked together to complete the canal within estimates.

The Panama Canal opened ahead of schedule on August 15, 1914. The total excavation for the channel exceeded 200 million cubic yards, of which almost half was taken from the Culebra Cut, later renamed Gaillard Cut in honor of the officer who conquered it, but who tragically died of a brain tumor in 1913 without seeing the canal's completion.

Army engineers retained a unique relationship with the Panama Canal after the canal was opened. Engineer officers traditionally served as the Governor and Lieutenant Governor of the Panama Canal Zone. The Governor also served as President of the Panama Canal Company, which was actually responsible for canal operations.

In the years immediately after the canal's completion, the Corps of Engineers accepted the responsibility for dredging the channel, which continued frequently to be blocked by landslides. Engineers finally determined the proper incline for the banks that provide the greatest insurance against slides. In the 1920s, the Corps further strengthened the banks by developing a system of drainage control. Still later, Army engineers helped enlarge the canal, although the original locks are still in use. One of the most unusual ways Army engineers assisted canal operations occurred in 1968, when the Corps sent the *Sturgis*, the world's first floating nuclear power plant, to the Canal Zone in order to alleviate dangerous reductions of electrical power caused by necessary curtailment of operations at the Gatun Hydroelectric Station. The weather had been so dry that there was not enough water to operate the locks as well as supply the turbines. The 10-megawatt floating station fulfilled a critical need, helping save over one trillion gallons of water for lock operations that otherwise would have been used for electrical generation.

Engineer officers have also periodically assisted in studies on other canal routes across Central America. Army engineers conducted a survey for a route across Nicaragua in the 1930s. In the 1960s, they were heavily involved in studies on an alternate Panamanian route that would accommodate larger vessels.

U.S. Army Engineers in World War I

1st Engineers, 1st Division, test a bridge in Gondrecourt, France, January 1918.

Office of History, Corps of Engineers

First ponton bridge across the Marne River, July 20, 1918.

Office of History, Corps of Engineers

Company E, 21st Engineers, operates a train near Ménil-la-Tour, Toul sector, France, March 1918.

Office of History, Corps of Engineers

World War I recruiting poster.

The Army Corps of Engineers was called upon during World War I to provide a much more diverse range of military services than had ever before been required. Not only did the engineers provide American combat divisions with the officers and men to staff the large 1,660-man engineer regiments that were part of each Army combat division, but they also built the port facilities, roads and railroads needed to bring essential war materiel to the front, harvested timber for military construction, employed searchlights in anti-aircraft defense, organized the first U.S. Army tank units, and developed chemical warfare munitions and defensive equipment. So important were these last pursuits that in 1918 a separate Tank Corps and a Chemical Warfare Service were created in the Army, the latter headed by an engineer officer.

The U.S. Army engineers who served in World War I brought with them varied amounts of experience with the military. Most senior engineer officers were graduates of the U.S. Military Academy and had previously served with U.S. Army

units abroad, primarily in Cuba or the Philippines. A few of them had accompanied General John Pershing in his expedition to Northern Mexico in 1916-17 that had unsuccessfully attempted to capture the Mexican revolutionary Pancho Villa after his raid on Columbus, New Mexico. Some engineer commanders had been civilian engineers who were members of the National Guard or Officers' Reserve Corps Engineer units organized a few years before the United States' entry into the war. But most of the 240,000 engineers who served in Europe during the war had no prior record of military service.

The British and French governments made the arrival of American engineers in France their top priority after the United States declared war on April 6, 1917. Thus, by the end of August 1917, nine newly organized engineer railway regiments, together with the engineer regiment of the 1st Division, had crossed the Atlantic and arrived in France. Several of the railway regiments were assigned to British or French military formations pending the arrival of larger numbers of American com-

79

Dugout entrance, Argonne, 1918.

Office of History, Corps of Engineers

bat troops in the summer and autumn of 1918. It was while serving with the British near the village of Gouzeaucourt, southwest of Cambrai, France, on September 5, 1917, that Sergeant Matthew Calderwood and Private William Branigan of the 11th Engineers were wounded by artillery fire, thereby becoming the first casualties in any U.S. Army unit serving at the front. When the Germans in late November 1917 launched a counteroffensive to regain territory they had just lost to the British near Cambrai, the men of the 11th Engineers abandoned their railway work and assisted the British to construct new defensive positions which stopped the German advance.

During 1918 U.S. Army engineers served in combat from the Vosges Mountains near the Swiss border north to Oudenaarde, Belgium. One battalion of the 310th Engineers even served in the Murmansk area of Northern Russia in a mission designed to assist Czech troops to rejoin the fighting on the Western front after Soviet Russia had left the war in March 1918. Most of this combat service consisted of the construction of bridges, roads and narrow-gauge (60 cm) railroads at or immediately behind the front, but engineer units also engaged in direct combat. Noteworthy among this combat service was the action of two companies of the 6th Engineers who ceased their construction of heavy steel bridges to join British and Canadian forces in front-line trenches where they together successfully defended Amiens from a heavy German assault in March and April 1918. These two engineer companies suffered a total of 77 casualties. During June and July 1918, troops of the 2d Engineers fought as infantry in their division's bitterly contested capture of the Belleau Woods and the nearby village of Vaux in the Aisne-Marne campaign. A battalion of the 1st Engineers fought as infantry in

the capture of Hill 269 in the Romagne Heights along the Hindenburg Line on October 8, 1918. It was for his action during this fighting that engineer Sergeant Wilbur E. Colyer of South Ozone, New York, was awarded the Medal of Honor. Colyer volunteered to locate a group of German machine-gun nests that was blocking the American advance. He used a captured

Office of History, Corps of Engineers

107th Engineers build a bridge in Cierges, France August 1918.

German grenade to kill one enemy machine-gunner, turned his machine gun against the other enemy nests, and silenced each of them.

Other U.S. Army engineers won personal recognition for their actions in bridging the Meuse River. Major William Hoge, Jr., a West Pointer serving with the 7th Engineers, 5th Division, won a Distinguished Service Cross for his heroism in reconnoitering a site for a ponton bridge across that well-defended waterway north of Brieulles, France. Hoge selected the bridge site during the daylight hours of November 4, 1918, while under enemy observation and artillery fire, and he directed the construction of the bridge that night. After German artillerists destroyed

three ponton boats supporting the bridge, engineer Sergeant Eugene Walker, Corporal Robert Crawford and Privates Noah Gump, John Hoggle and Stanley Murnane jumped into the icy river and held up the deck of the bridge until replacement pontons could be launched and installed. These enlisted men were also awarded the Distinguished Service Cross. This

French officers train
American troops.

Maintaining High Standards: The
2d Engineers in France, 1918
  During World War I, the 2d Engineer Regiment of the 2d "Indian
Head" Infantry Division, commanded successively by Colo-
nels James F. McIndoe and
William A. Mitchell, was considered one of the best regiments in
the American Expeditionary
Forces (AEF) in France. Because of its bloody engagements
at Belleau Woods, Château
Thierry, Soissons and Meuse-
Argonne, the division's infantry
units sustained the highest percentage of major casualties to its
strength among all AEF units—
its 30.38 percent casualty rate
just edging the 30.08 percentage
of the "Big Red 1," 1st Infantry Division. The 2d Engineers, moreover, stood 15th in the list of
casualties with 12.73 percent, by
far the highest of any engineer
unit. The reasons were simple—
the trench war was preeminently
an engineer's war, cutting
barbed wire entanglements,
putting them up, digging dug-
outs, machine gun positions and
trenches and all too often fighting
as infantry.
  Throughout its time in combat
the regiment maintained high
morale and unexcelled performance in all its assignments. An
unnamed American general officer said that "the 2d Engineers
is the best regiment I ever saw
. . . The regiment has assisted
the artillery, has helped the
tanks, built railroads, manned
machine guns and fought time
after time as infantry. That regiment can do anything." One rea-
son for its excellent performance
was the high standards its officers and men required of themselves and each other. These
standards applied throughout the
regiment and were vigorously enforced.

Company D, 11th
Engineers, builds
a road near the
Aire River.

U.S. Army tractor
negotiates a steep grade
on the Rhine at Coblenz,
Germany.

bridge was one of 38 constructed by
U.S. Army Engineers during the
critical Meuse-Argonne offensive,
which ended with the German military collapse.
  U.S. Army engineers also made
essential contributions to ultimate
victory well behind the front lines.
The forestry troops of the 20th
Engineers, the U.S. Army's largest
regiment, produced roughly 200
million feet of lumber in France,
together with some three million
standard-gauge railroad ties and
one million narrow-gauge ties.
American troops, under the technical supervision of Army engineers,
used this lumber in the construction
of new and expanded port facilities
for American ships, including
berths for deep-draft vessels at
Brest that were the only ones
available to U.S. vessels; storage
depots containing more than
15 million square feet of covered
storage space; new hospitals
containing more than 140,000
beds; and barracks capable of
housing 742,000 men. Engineer
troops constructed 950 miles
of standard-gauge rail lines,
primarily at docks and storage
yards; water supply facilities at
several French ports and communications centers; and 90 miles of new
roads. During the war U.S. Army
engineers drew and printed maps,
conducted geological studies with
an eye to underground water supplies, installed and operated electrical lines and mechanical equipment, and experimented with the
use of tractors and trailers for haul-
ing ponton bridging equipment in
the absence of sufficient animals.
American engineers also operated
seven cement plants in France.
These varied facilities permitted the
U.S. Army to field and support a
force of nearly two million men in
France within 20 months of the
nation's entry into the war.

Combat Engineers in World War II

Amphibious engineers put assault troops ashore on Wakde Island, New Guinea, May 18, 1944.

167th Engineer Combat Battalion, 1117th Engineer Group, builds the first Bailey bridge across the Rhine at Wesel, Germany, March 26, 1945.

Half-tracks cross the Seine on a ponton bridge, August 1944.

As Japanese forces pressed their attacks in China and Hitler increased his territorial demands in Central Europe in mid-1939, the U.S. Army Corps of Engineers numbered less than 800 officers and 6,000 enlisted men in active Regular Army service. During the preceding 17 years, since the withdrawal in 1922 of engineer troops from Coblenz, Germany, where they had occupied territory along the Rhine River, the Army had maintained in active service only eight or nine combat engineer regiments, two engineer squadrons and a single topographic battalion. It staffed even this short troop list at only some 70 percent of authorized strength. Engineer officers thus spent most of their time during the 1920s and 1930s administering the Corps' civil works program, whose budget in 1938 was nearly 400 times greater than its military budget.

Engineer military mobilization began in earnest in mid-1940 after the German conquest of France. During late 1940 and early 1941 the Army inducted 18 National Guard divisions, each containing an engi-

neer combat regiment, and their men began to undergo intensive training. The Army quickly organized engineer aviation companies and battalions to build the airfields needed to defend the Western Hemisphere. Blacks joined the Army in unprecedented numbers in 1940 and 1941, and many were assigned to engineer units. Black soldiers, who numbered 20 percent of Corps personnel by the war's end, were assigned to segregated units usually in the construction field, but they were trained by white officers such as Major (later General) Andrew Goodpaster.

Initiated well before the attack at Pearl Harbor, engineer research and development projects directed by the Engineer Board at Fort Belvoir, Virginia, would have a significant impact upon the war. Experiments conducted during 1940 and 1941 developed a light and inexpensive pierced-steel plank mat that the Army Air Forces would widely use to provide safe, stable landing fields for American planes. Spurred by the ideas of Engineer Captain (later General) Bruce Clarke, Engineer Board studies perfected a new

Office of History, Corps of Engineers

Demolition squad probes
for Japanese mines.

steel treadway bridge constructed
on pneumatic floats that would
carry heavy modern tanks across
the rivers of Europe. And it was the
Engineer Board that produced by
1943 a tank dozer capable of knock-
ing over substantial barriers while
conducting an armored assault.

When the Japanese bombed
military bases in Hawaii and the
Philippines on the morning of December 7, 1941, engineer units that
had already been deployed to those
islands were called upon to respond
a few hours later. The 34th Engineers, a combat regiment which
had lost some equipment but no
casualties during the bombing in
Hawaii, worked to maintain roads
that were suffering from heavy military traffic. The skimpy, 1,500-man
U.S. Army engineer garrison in the
Philippines was almost evenly divided between Filipino and American personnel. After Japanese
forces landed there on December
10, the engineers destroyed bridges
from one end of Luzon to the other
to slow the enemy's advance. The
engineers later erected a series of
defensive lines on the Bataan Peninsula and fought as infantry in
these defenses before succumbing
to superior Japanese forces in April
and May 1942. In the southern Philippines, a number of Army engineers escaped to the mountains of
Mindanao, where they worked with
Filipino guerrillas and remained active throughout the period of Japanese occupation of the Philippines.

U.S. Army engineers first entered combat against German and
Italian forces in North Africa,
where they landed in November
1942. During the first five months
of 1943, a few units of American
engineers assisted U.S. Army
movements in the broad deserts
and fields of Tunisia, clearing enemy
mines and building roads from
scratch. Prior to the American
attacks on Gafsa and Maknassy
in the barren plains of southern

Tunisia, the 1st Engineer Combat
Battalion and a company of the
19th Engineer Combat Regiment
built combat approach roads
through a no-man's land between
the combatants, where they were
vulnerable to surprise attacks.

After the Allied victory in
North Africa, American and British
forces landed first in Sicily and then

Defense Audio-Visual Agency

1st Battalion, 355th
Engineers, clears St. Lo for
Omaha Beach traffic.

in continental Italy during the summer of 1943. Defended by well-
equipped and determined German
forces, Italy's mountainous terrain
and rapidly flowing rivers chal-
lenged the road- and bridge-building
skills of the Army engineers. The
combat engineers particularly distinguished themselves in the fighting at and just south of the Rapido
River in the Army's drive north
from Naples. The 48th and 235th

Engineer Combat Battalions, assigned to an armored task force under Brigadier General Frank Allen
that was ordered to capture Mount
Porchia just south of the Rapido,
not only removed obstacles and
opened supply lines but also fought
as infantry on the flanks of the task
force's advance. After enemy fire
had substantially reduced the armored infantry units leading this
attack, the 48th was ordered to

General Dwight D. Eisenhower exhorts paratroopers on D-day, June 6, 1944.

Office of History, Corps of Engineers

Exploiting Enemy Mistakes: Army Engineers, Meter Beams, and the Advance into Germany.

When the Germans withdrew from northern France in the summer and fall of 1944, they left Cherbourg harbor a shambles. A massive reconstruction job faced engineers with the American forces who occupied the city. The difficulty of obtaining adequate construction materials from the United States only exacerbated the problem. The situation demanded prompt and ingenious improvisation and the Advance Section (ADSEC) Engineers of the Communications Zone were up to the task.

The enemy had made a big mistake at Cherbourg and the engineers turned it to their advantage. Lieutenant General Emerson C. Itschner (Ret.), then a colonel and ADSEC Engineer, recalled the situation: "The Germans were kind enough to leave us a lot of very heavy steel beams, one meter in depth and up to 75 feet long. We had enough of these to bridge from the piles that we drove back to the seawall."

Exploitation of the mistake did not stop with the reopening of the port of Cherbourg. The ADSEC engineers noted that all of the beams bore the name of a single steel mill, Hadir in Differdange, Luxembourg. Right then Itschner decided they would head for Differdange. So, as soon as the town fell, the ADSEC men were there. They were not disappointed: the Hadir plant was intact and the citizens were eager to reopen it. After a little repair and cannibalization, Hadir began once again to produce meter beams. In a short time these beams were put to many important uses including the construction of the massive railroad bridges across the Rhine.

Thus did engineer alertness and ingenuity solve a major supply problem.

secure the top and sides of the mountain. It was in this effort that engineer Sergeant Joe Specker of Odessa, Missouri, having observed an enemy machine-gun nest and several well-placed snipers blocking his company's progress, advanced alone with a machine gun up the rocky slope. Although mortally wounded by intense enemy fire, Specker nevertheless set up and fired his weapon so effectively that the enemy machine gun was silenced and the snipers were forced to withdraw. With this assistance the battalion was able to clear the summit of Mount Porchia. Sergeant Specker was honored by a posthumous award of the Medal of Honor.

More than a dozen U.S. Army Engineer combat battalions landed on the beaches of Normandy during the Allies' assault landing on June 6, 1944. The engineers cleared the beach obstacles and minefields that the Germans had implanted there, absorbing on Omaha Beach substantial casualties including the loss of two battalion commanders. Bulldozer drivers, often working in the face of heavy enemy fire, opened exits up narrow draws through the cliffs lining the beaches. Some of the engineers quickly engaged in combat with the Germans alongside assault infantry teams. In one such action, Lieutenant Robert Ross of the 37th Engineer Combat Battalion took charge of an infantry company that had lost its leaders and led it and his own engineer platoon up the slopes adjoining Omaha Beach, where they killed 40 Germans and captured two machine gun emplacements.

The engineers again provided critical support to the achievement and exploitation of the breakthrough that American forces created in late July 1944 in enemy defenses southwest of St. Lo, France. Army and divisional engineer troops repaired roads and

Connecting sections of 100-foot "snake" torpedo to pulling tank, Gorze, France.

Office of History, Corps of Engineers

cleared enemy mine fields in and beyond St. Lo with exceptional speed, and they rapidly bridged the small rivers in the area to maintain the Americans' momentum. After the German line had been effectively pierced, armored division engineers constructed the treadway bridges needed by Patton's tanks in the Third Army's quick pursuit of the retreating Germans across northern France. Engineer general service regiments behind them rapidly reconstructed or replaced railroad bridges that had been destroyed by the retreating Germans. In Lorraine the 130th Engineer General Service Regiment successfully built under heavy artillery fire a 190-foot-long double-triple Bailey bridge that Third Army troops used to cross the Moselle at Thionville, France. This bridge had to reach 10 feet longer than the specified maximum span of such a bridge, but it successfully carried heavy American tanks.

The massive German offensive in the Ardennes forest that began on December 16, 1944, exacted a heavy toll among the sparse American forces surprised in the area. A disproportionate number of those troops were engineers who had been operating sawmills or repairing forest roads, and of necessity these engineer troops were called upon to fight as infantry. The 81st Engineer Combat Battalion, which had been engaged in road maintenance around Auw, Germany, quickly found itself caught in the center of the powerful enemy assault, and

Treadway bridge lowered into place near Moderscheid, Belgium, January 1945.

within a week the Germans had captured or killed a majority of its troops despite their determined combat, notably in the defense of St. Vith, Belgium.

Colonel H. W. Anderson's 1111th Engineer Combat Group was headquartered at Trois Ponts, Belgium, right on the path of Joachim Peiper's fast-moving assault tank group. Despite their inferior numbers, Anderson's engineers put up a stout and effective resistance which crippled Peiper's force. A mine field hastily laid by a squad of the 291st Engineer Combat Battalion before Stavelot delayed Peiper's entry into that town overnight. On the following day, December 18, engineers from that battalion helped deflect the German tank column away from the critical petroleum depot near Francorchamps, located on the road to Spa where the First Army had its headquarters. A company of the 51st Engineer Combat Battalion then diverted the column again at Trois Ponts by blowing the bridges there and defending the village alone until airborne troops could reinforce it. Peiper's tanks eventually ran out of fuel well short of his Meuse River objective, and Peiper's men had to abandon them.

To the south, elements of the 44th, 103d, and 159th Engineer Combat Battalions delayed portions of the German Fifth and Seventh Armies at the villages of Wiltz, Hosingen and Scheidgen in Luxembourg, before German forces overwhelmed their positions. While ultimately unsuccessful, the defense undertaken by these engineer units delayed enemy forces long enough to permit American infantry, airborne and armored units to come to the defense of critically located Bastogne. Engineer troops also fought before Bastogne, some using anti-tank weapons with which they had no experience. Private Bernard Michin of the 158th Engineer Combat Battalion waited until an enemy tank came within 10 yards of him before having sufficient assurance of his target to fire a bazooka at it. The resulting explosion temporarily blinded him. He rolled into a ditch and, hearing enemy machinegun fire, lobbed a hand grenade toward its source. The firing stopped abruptly. Michin was awarded a Distinguished Service Cross.

Members of 166th Engineers, sanding a highway with mechanical spreader. Near Wiltz, Luxembourg–1945.

Telling It Like It Is

Some folks accuse Army engineers of patting themselves on the back. If, at times, they do seem boastful, it may be because they have something to boast about.

At a convention of the American Historical Association in the late 1940s, Dr. O. J. Clinard, then the Corps of Engineers' chief historian, was in a cocktail lounge with friends. After a few drinks, Clinard started extolling the glories of the Corps and was soon reeling off a list of engineer "greats":

Sylvanus Thayer, "father of West Point"

John C. Frémont, "pathfinder of the West"

Gouverneur K. Warren, hero of Gettysburg

George W. Goethals, builder of the Panama Canal

Charles G. Dawes, vice president of the U.S. under Coolidge

Lucius D. Clay, post-war governor of Germany

At that, a friend broke in: "Hold on, old buddy. Next you'll be telling us that Robert E. Lee and Douglas MacArthur—our greatest soldiers—were Army engineers."

Clinard beamed.

"Go look 'em up," he said.

Office of History, Corps of Engineers

Engineers operate infantry assault ferry across the Neckar River in Heilbronn, Germany, April 1945.

Office of History, Corps of Engineers

Placing explosive charges on concrete tank barriers along the Siegfried Line, October 1944.

American forces pushed a badly weakened German army out of the Ardennes in January 1945 and advanced to the river barriers of the Roer and Rhine. Relying on Army engineer bridging skills, the U.S. Army crossed the Roer on February 23, 1945, before floodwaters released by the breaking of upstream dams had subsided, thus surprising the Germans and permitting a rapid American advance. Engineers also played a critical role in the surprising capture of the Ludendorff railroad bridge across the Rhine at Remagen on March 7. As elements of the armored combat command under career engineer officer Brigadier General William M. Hoge, Jr., approached the bridge that afternoon, the Germans set off a charge of dynamite in an unsuccessful attempt to destroy the span. Risking a new explosion, Lieutenant Hugh Mott, Sergeant Eugene Dorland and Sergeant John Reynolds, all members of Company B, 9th Armored Engineer Battalion, ran onto the bridge in the company of assault infantrymen. The engineers first located four 30-pound packages of explosives tied to I-beams under the decking, cut these free, and sent them splashing into the Rhine. After the infantry had cleared the far-shore bridge towers, Sergeant Dorland found the master switch for some 500 pounds of intended bridge demolition explosives, and he quickly shot out the heavy wires leading from it. Lieutenant Mott then directed under continuing heavy enemy fire the repair of the bridge's planking, and seven hours later he reported that tanks could cross.

While nine U.S. Army divisions crossed the Rhine at Remagen, most U.S. forces crossed that broad river in assaults in late March 1945 that were supported by the combat

The "Robert Gouldin" railway bridge across the Rhine River in Germany, built by Army Engineers in ten days in early April 1945.

First jeep to cross ponton bridge over the Meuse near Houx, Belgium, September 1944.

bridge-building endeavors of the Corps of Engineers. Engineer boatmen piloted Navy landing craft to carry assault units across the swift-flowing Rhine. Behind them other engineers began installing numerous heavy ponton and treadway bridges that would securely tie the assaulting troops to their sources of supply. Third Army engineers built a 1,896-foot-long treadway bridge across the Rhine at Mainz under combat conditions. Further south, Seventh Army engineers completed in a scant nine-and-a-quarter hours a 1,047-foot ponton bridge across the Rhine at Worms. Heavy enemy fire delayed completion of some bridges and exacted casualties. Captain Harold Love, commander of an engineer treadway bridge company, was killed when the treadway section he was ferrying to a partially completed bridge at Milchplatz was struck by a German shell. After crossing the Rhine, the Western Allies pushed rapidly across Germany toward their rendezvous with the Russians at the Elbe River. When the Soviet army arrived in Magdeburg in May, they found that Ninth Army engineers had already on April 13 built a treadway bridge across the Elbe at Barby 15 miles south of that east German city.

In the fighting against Japanese forces in the Pacific U.S. Army engineers distinguished themselves notably during the amphibious landings that they supported. The engineer boat and shore regiments of the 2d, 3d and 4th Engineer Special Brigades directed a series of landings on the north coast of New Guinea and on nearby New Britain, Los Negros, Biak and Morotai Islands as U.S. and Australian forces advanced by sea in a step-by-step fashion toward their October 1944 return to Leyte Island in the Philippines. The engineer boatmen who brought ashore a task force of the 41st Infantry Division at Nassau Bay, New Guinea, on June 30,

1943, found themselves engaged in hand-to-hand combat with a much larger Japanese force assaulting the beaches just one day after the landing. Demonstrating their skill with knife and bayonet, the engineers held their portion of the beach perimeter. After the Allies captured the Japanese base at Finschhafen three months later, U.S. Army shore engineers operating the beach depot two miles north of that New Guinea town were surprised by a Japanese landing attempt before dawn on October 17, 1943. Here engineer gunner Junior Van Noy, a 19-year-old private from Idaho, refused to heed calls to withdraw from his shoreside machine gun position despite heavy enemy attacks on it with grenades, flame throwers, and rifle fire. Van Noy managed to expend his entire stock of ammunition on the fast-approaching Japanese before succumbing to enemy fire. He is thought to have alone killed at least half of the 39 enemy troops that had disembarked. Van Noy was honored with a posthumous award of the Medal of Honor.

Engineer combat forces also participated in maneuver warfare on land against the Japanese. On May 29-30, 1943, the Japanese that had been surrounded by U.S. Army forces on Attu Island in the Aleutians attempted to break through the portion of the American lines held by an engineer combat company, but they were decisively repulsed. The unit killed 53 of the enemy while having only one officer killed and one enlisted man wounded in the battle. In the Philippines, the 302d Engineer Combat Battalion, responsible for road maintenance across rice paddies and swamps near Ormoc on Leyte, built or reinforced 52 bridges for tank traffic in mid-December 1944, generally working under small-arms and mortar fire, and contributed men and armored bulldoz-

ers to flush enemy troops out of their foxholes in the bamboo thicket. In northern Luzon and on Mindanao in the Philippines in early 1945 divisional engineer battalions completed essential road and bridge-building projects in difficult mountainous terrain that sometimes rose higher than 4,000 feet above sea level. The 106th Engineer Combat Battalion on Mindanao constructed a 425-foot infantry support bridge across the Pulangi River and, encountering a gorge 120 feet across and 35 feet deep, blasted out its sides to create in a speedy fashion a crude rock bridge. Much of the engineer construction work on Luzon and Mindanao was also interrupted by enemy fire.

During World War II the U.S. Army Corps of Engineers contributed essential military services wherever the U.S. Army was deployed.

Private Junior N. Van Noy.

Working on a Bailey bridge over the Magampon River, Luzon, the Philippines, April 3, 1945.

89

The Manhattan Project

S-50 thermal diffusion plant under construction.

Hanford plant.

The Manhattan Project was the United States' effort to develop an atomic weapon during World War II. In three short years, the project brought atomic weaponry from scientific hypothesis to reality.

Following the discovery of nuclear fission in Germany in 1930, physicists the world over began experimenting to determine if neutrons were released during fission and, if so, how they might be utilized to create a chain reaction. If controlled in a reactor, such a chain reaction would be a great power source. If uncontrolled, it could produce an explosion far greater than any from chemical explosives.

The initial effort to hasten the progress of atomic research in the United States came from the scientific community. A small group of European scientists had settled in the United States after fleeing from Nazism in the late thirties. They were well aware of the atomic research being done in Germany and fearing that Germany would produce an atomic bomb first, they prevailed upon Albert Einstein to persuade President Roosevelt to increase funding for atomic research and development.

After America's entry into the war in December 1941, researchers from the Allied nations joined the effort. The Allies drew up formal agreements on atomic cooperation and a scientific military intelligence unit was established to follow German progress in atomic research.

91

Public Affairs Office, Corps of Engineers

General Groves recognizes
Oppenheimer.

By the spring of 1942, research had progressed to the point that an atomic weapon actually seemed possible. The National Defense Research Committee, then coordinating atomic research and headed by Vannevar Bush, began to formulate plans for the construction of production facilities. The U.S. Army Corps of Engineers, designated by the Committee to oversee the program, provided the technical expertise required for this mammoth construction project.

On June 18, 1942, Major General W. D. Styer, Chief of Staff for Army Services of Supply, directed Colonel James C. Marshall of the Corps of Engineers to form a new engineer district. The district was to carry out the Corps' new responsibility for construction for the project.

The new district's offices were initially located in Manhattan at the headquarters of the Corps' New York District. The name "Manhattan" stuck. It seemed to be a name

Mushroom cloud from test
detonation on Bikini Atoll,
July 1, 1946.

Joint Task Force 1, U.S. Army

First pile area at Hanford Works.

that would arouse the least suspicion, for the district, the project and its super-secret mission.

By September, Major General Leslie R. Groves, formerly Deputy Chief of the Construction Division in the Corps, had been named by Secretary of War Stimson to direct the entire project. Scientific direction remained with the National Defense Research Committee within the Office of Scientific Research and Development that Vannevar Bush headed.

As research continued in the fall of 1942, Groves and Marshall began to select sites for the atomic material production plants. The sites all had to be isolated so they could be sealed off for tight security. They all needed great quantities of both water and electricity. An additional site also had to be found at which scientists could finally assemble the weapons.

At the recommendation of Groves and Marshall, the government purchased 83,000 acres of land near Clinton, Tennessee, for the Clinton Engineer Works (later called Oak Ridge). Here the Corps built uranium separation plants to separate the fissionable isotope Uranium-235 from the isotope more prevalent in uranium ore, Uranium-238. Army engineers also constructed residential communities to house employees.

In December 1942, when Enrico Fermi produced a controlled chain reaction at the University of Chicago, he discovered a new material suitable for fission. He found that during the chain reaction Uranium-238 could capture neutrons and be transformed into plutonium, a new element as unstable as Uranium-235. Twelve days after Fermi's successful experiment, Groves discussed building a plutonium plant site with scientists and industry and Corps representatives. The government soon purchased almost a half million acres around Hanford,

Washington, near Bonneville Dam for the construction of five plutonium reactors and employee housing.

Besides building huge industrial plants and providing the most basic community needs of water, roads, sanitation, housing and power, the Corps also managed the construction of scientific equipment, newly designed and as yet untried. At both Hanford and Oak Ridge the project requirements were initially underestimated. At Oak Ridge alone the cost of the land was $4 million. Construction costs at Oak Ridge by December 31, 1946, totalled $304 million. Research at this site eventually totalled $20 million, engineering $6 million, and operation $204 million. Power for operation alone cost $10 million. Instead of requiring a work force of 2,500 people as was originally planned, Oak Ridge eventually had 24,000 employees on the payroll.

As work continued at Oak Ridge and Hanford, General Groves appointed J. Robert Oppenheimer to take charge of the newly created weapons laboratory in an isolated desert area around Los Alamos, New Mexico. Here scientists assembled the weapons. The first explosion of an atomic bomb occurred here.

The engineering problems encountered in the project were numerous. Groves and his staff fought constantly for needed raw materials. The engineers continually had to translate the scientists' theories into precise specifications. New materials had to be formulated for the building of the reactors and the separation equipment. Contractors were held to extremely exacting specifications for everything they supplied.

The Corps' engineering role required the simultaneous coordination of construction with research and new discoveries. It required the building of huge industrial facilities

along with community public works needed to provide a livable environment for the employees. It required the transportation of goods to these isolated areas, the management of huge amounts of money and the coordination of input from hundreds of contractors.

The project also required the maintenance of a delicate relationship between the military and the scientific communities. Workers and scientists had relocated to physically isolated areas and because of the secrecy of their work, had to limit their contact with the outside world. Even in wartime, when the work had a special urgency and sacrifices were made for the war effort, morale was a great concern. The scientists especially were uncomfortable under the military supervision and security restrictions. Very few of the thousands of employees on the project knew what they were actually working on because of the strict security. The employees did share, however, in the anxiety over the unknown dangers inherent in the materials they dealt with. No one dreamed at the beginning how massive the project would become and that its cost by war's end would total $2 billion. Very few realized the tremendous impact the project would have on the world.

Engineer Combat in Korea and Vietnam

Bridging the Hantan River along the central front, April 1951.

Sergeant George Libby.

Surveying for a shorter ammunition supply route, December 1951.

Building a Bailey bridge in Vietnam.

The rugged terrain of the Korean peninsula and the numerical superiority of enemy forces there made engineer construction and combat vital to the U.S. Army during the Korean War. Surprised by the North Korean attack across the 38th parallel, U.S. Army troops in Korea and the Republic of Korea's forces could at first do no more than delay the advance of the larger North Korean forces. U.S. Army engineers played a major role in this delaying action, mining roads and destroying key bridges. In this early fighting, engineers were frequently called upon to do tasks not traditionally theirs. Thus it was members of Company C, 3d Engineer Combat Battalion, that on July 20, 1950, made the first verifiable combat use near Taejon of the newly developed 3.5-inch rocket launcher, using it to destroy a tank that was threatening their division commander.

Attempting to withdraw from Taejon that evening, U.S. forces were stopped for a time by enemy roadblocks. Engineer Sergeant George Libby placed wounded men on an artillery tractor and used his body to shield its driver as it crashed through two enemy roadblocks before reaching American lines to the south. Libby, who died of his wounds, was posthumously awarded the Medal of Honor.

After U.S. Army engineers destroyed the bridges over the wide Naktong River in the southeastern corner of Korea on August 2-3,

95

Engineers prepare to blow a bridge in North Korea, to slow enemy advance, December 1950.

1950, the outnumbered American forces maintained a long defensive perimeter around Pusan as General Douglas MacArthur prepared to land a large body of U.S. troops behind enemy lines at Inchon. Engineers were frequently committed to fight as infantry on the Pusan perimeter. Private Melvin Brown of the 8th Engineer Combat Battalion was awarded the Medal of Honor for bravely holding his position on a wall of the ancient fortress of Kasan during an enemy assault. After he had expended his ammunition, Private Brown used his entrenching tool to repel the armed attackers as they reached the top of the wall.

After MacArthur's assault at Inchon had caught the enemy by surprise, U.S. forces soon took the offensive across Korea. The bridge building and road and rail repairs undertaken by the Army engineers allowed U.S. and allied forces to push north rapidly in pursuit of the disintegrating North Korean army. Handicapped at first by tremendous shortages of supplies, these construction efforts required the engineers to make innovative use of available materials. When Chinese units began their powerful counteroffensive in November 1950, the engineers had to destroy many of the same bridges as U.S. forces again retreated south of Seoul. But lateral roads built by the engineers behind the new defensive lines proved critical when the Chinese broke through a portion of that line. These roads enabled the Americans to transport the 3d Infantry Division 100 miles in a single day to plug the hole that the Chinese had created.

As U.S. forces returned to the offensive in mountainous central Korea in early 1951, engineer units blasted cliffsides to build new roads and built aerial tramways to carry supplies to the troops. When the advancing 23d Regimental Combat Team and a French battalion were

surrounded at Chipyong-ni on February 13, 1951, by an attacking force apparently comprised of three Chinese divisions, the engineer company supporting the combat team fought as infantry to assist it to withstand the attacks until an American armored relief column could reach the town two days later. In early October 1951, the 2d Engineer Combat Battalion converted a rough track leading north to Mundung-ni into a road usable by tanks, enabling an American tank battalion to surprise a Chinese column attempting to relieve hard-pressed Chinese troops on Heartbreak Ridge near the 38th parallel. This interception eased the capture of the ridge by U.S. and French forces. An Army engineer construc-

three U.S. Army divisions. After installing two temporary floating bridges, Army engineer troops built at the less critical site an innovative low-level bridge sturdy enough to survive if overtopped by flood waters. In the center of the I Corps line, the 84th Engineer Construction Battalion erected within range of the enemy's artillery a modern commercial-type highway bridge utilizing sheet-pile cofferdams and reinforced concrete piers. Dedicated to engineer Medal of Honor winner George Libby, that bridge remains in use and retains its tactical significance 30 years after its construction. In sum, the U.S. Army engineers in Korea compiled a very creditable record of combat and wartime construction that comple-

Building a "scrounge bridge" across the Pukhan River, April 1951.

tion battalion supported the 1st Marine Division in its combat in mountainous central Korea during much of 1951.

The engineers confronted a critical challenge after the summer floods of July 1952 washed out two of the five high-level bridges across the Imjin River, located a mere four miles behind the battle lines of

96

YAH-64 helicopter with anti-armor battle dress.

mented and often multiplied the combat effectiveness of the highly motorized U.S. forces engaged there.

The Army again called upon its engineers for combat support in Asia to assist the Republic of Vietnam. As in northern Korea, where Chinese troops had hidden their movements prior to their November 1950 offensive, in South Vietnam anti-government forces relied heavily upon a strategy of concealment in their combat with U.S. forces. U.S. Army operations in Vietnam thus did not occur along a well-defined front line but could break out wherever the Americans encountered guerrilla forces or North Vietnamese troops. The elusiveness of the enemy in Vietnam led U.S. Army engineers to alter in several ways the manner in which they pursued their task of enhancing the combat environment of friendly forces.

Search and destroy missions were frequently employed by American forces to attack areas of particular enemy strength. The 1st Engineer Battalion supported Operation Rolling Stone in Binh Duong Province near Saigon by building a road into the Iron Triangle and War Zone D, two staging areas frequently used by the Viet Cong. Men of this battalion engaged in a half-hour-long firefight with the enemy on February 26, 1966. The following summer a 52-bulldozer battalion task force cleared 2,700 acres of jungle, destroyed 6 miles of enemy tunnels, and demolished 11 factories and villages in the Iron Triangle.

The wide use of helicopter transport in Vietnam enabled U.S. forces to respond quickly to enemy attacks anywhere in Vietnam. After South Vietnamese forces relieved a besieged Special Forces camp at Plei Me in the Central Highlands in October 1965, an engineer company of the airmobile 1st Cavalry Division lengthened and improved an earthen airfield at a nearby tea plantation using equipment brought in by helicopter. The division then pursued the attacking North Vietnamese regiments west from Plei Me through the jungles of the Highlands. The division relied for forward supply and reinforcement in this campaign upon helicopter landing zones that divisional engineers quickly cleared

Engineer mine-sweeping team.

Combat engineers of
173d Airborne Brigade
search Ding Nai River
for underwater bridge.

from the jungle using chain saws
and demolitions. By the time that
the North Vietnamese forces engaged in this fight reached the safety
of Cambodia, they had lost 1,800
men. During the next 10 months
the 8th Engineer Battalion built
seven airfields for the division in
the Highlands, including one at a
site eight miles from the Cambodian
border to which all construction
equipment, supplies and personnel
had to be transported by helicopter.
The battalion could do this because
engineer planners had modified procurement orders for large earthmov-
ing equipment to obtain machinery
that could be disassembled for air-
lift and then quickly reassembled.

Various technological innovations aided the Army engineers
in Vietnam. To combat the thick
mud that could quickly disable the
Army's tactical airfields in the
monsoon season, the engineers
employed the new T-17 membrane,
a neoprene-coated fabric which they
used to cover the airfields and provide them with an impermeable
"raincoat." The engineers sprayed

Installing T-17 membrane
at Bao Loc.

Office of History, Corps of Engineers

Engineer and Rome Plow of 60th Land Clearing Company.

peneprime, a dust palliative with an asphaltic base, onto heliport sites during the dry season to prevent dust clouds from interfering with helicopter operations.

The use by guerrilla forces of the thick forests along the nation's major transportation routes to conceal themselves before laying mines or staging ambushes impelled the engineers to clear all vegetation up to 100 yards on either side of major roadways. Finding bulldozers and flammable napalm unequal to the task, the engineers in 1967 introduced the Rome Plow, a military tractor equipped with a protective cab and a special tree-cutting blade that was sharpened daily. Lieutenant General Julian Ewell, a high field commander in Vietnam, called the Rome Plow "the most effective device" in his arsenal. A land-clearing engineer company equipped with 30 Rome Plows could clear 180-200 acres of medium density jungle each day.

The enemy's Tet Offensive early in 1968 closed for over a month several critical roads, particularly in the northern part of the Republic of Vietnam. The Army's 35th Engineer Battalion, which had concentrated on road building during its previous service in Vietnam, reopened coastal Route 1 north of Da Nang in late February 1968 while assigned to the III Marine Amphibious Force. By this time the engineers had built a sufficient number of airfields, heliports, and troop cantonments to permit them to continue to concentrate on road construction. The 27th Engineer Battalion now built a new all-weather highway from Hue west to the A Shau valley, an enemy stronghold. Engineer units in the Mekong Delta developed a clay-lime coagulation process that they used there to build durable roads from locally available materials. The engineers protected their bridges by installing extensive lighting systems and anti-swimmer and anti-mine devices using concertina wire and booms. Overall, Army engineer troops constructed roughly 900 miles of modern, paved highways connecting the major population centers of the Republic of Vietnam. Engineer officers also monitored the construction by private American contractors of an additional 550 miles of Vietnamese highways.

Army engineers also undertook certain responsibilities for installation security and these could involve heroic individual actions. When an enemy team infiltrated the base of the 173d Engineer Company at Camp Radcliff at An Khe in the Central Highlands on March 20, 1969, Engineer Corporal Terry Kawamura threw himself on an explosive charge that had been hurled into his quarters absorbing its blast and thereby protecting other members of his unit endangered in the attack. Corporal Kawamura was posthumously awarded a Medal of Honor.

A half-dozen Army engineer battalions participated in the Cambodian incursion in May and June of 1970. Engineers built 35 miles of new roads, 23 fixed bridges and 25 fire support bases during the attack on North Vietnamese supply points and staging areas within Cambodia. During this period the senior Army engineer officer in Vietnam, Major General John Dillard, and two other high ranking Army engineers were killed when their helicopter was shot down southwest of Pleiku. These losses were illustrative of the dedicated support which the Corps of Engineers gave to the Army during its service in Vietnam.

Defense Audio-Visual Agency

Engineer tunnel demolition team.

Military Construction

Arnold Engineering
Development Center,
Tullahoma, Tennessee,
built for the Air Force.

Soldiers of the 95th Engineer
General Service Regiment
building a bridge on the
Alaska Highway.

Pentagon under construction
in 1942.

The military construction mission of the Corps of Engineers dates from the early days of World War II. Prior to that time, the Quartermaster Department built almost all Army facilities. By 1940 it was clear that this arrangement could not continue. Quartermaster resources were inadequate for the large mobilization job ahead. On the other hand, the engineers' civil works organization and experience provided the basis for absorption of the assignment. So, in November 1940, the War Department chose the Corps to build facilities for the Army Air Corps. Thirteen months later, the Corps undertook all construction for the Army's war effort.

This massive enterprise involved military and industrial projects. The Corps managed construction of a wide range of factories, most notably for the assembly of aircraft and tanks and the production of ammunition. Military installations included camps for 5.3 million soldiers, depots, ports and the Pentagon. Each of these tasks included planning, site selection, land acquisition, design, contract negoti-

ations, procurement, labor relations and the construction itself. All told, the wartime mobilization program involved more than 27,000 projects and cost $15.3 billion, or approximately $100 billion in 1980 dollars. Lieutenant General Leslie R. Groves, head of the Manhattan Project, summed up the significance of this work for the successful conduct of the war: "Mobilization was decisive and construction generally controlled mobilization."

Yet there was more to engineer construction during the war than the stateside program. Work in support of the war against Japan ranged over a vast portion of the world, from Panama to India and from Alaska to Australia. A huge organization, which grew to include 236,000 engineer troops in an Army of 1,455,000, built pipelines, dredged harbors and built and repaired ports throughout the Pacific theater. Some of the accomplishments in this region rivaled those of the Corps on the home front.

Among the major projects in the Pacific area was the air ferry route to the Philippines. To move heavy bombers west across the

Fitzsimons Army Hospital, Denver, 1952.

ocean, the Corps built airfields on a host of Pacific islands. The engineers developed these bases in a matter of a few months.

Two land routes also merit special notice. The Alcan Highway, prompted by the threat of a Japanese invasion and the closure of Alaskan sea routes, ran over 1,500 miles of muskeg and mountains.

The project involved 133 major bridges and at the peak of construction employed 81 contractors and 14,000 men. Closer to the war, the Ledo Road from northeastern India to Burma crossed 430 miles of jungle, mountains and rivers. Alongside went the longest invasion pipeline ever built.

The war against Germany also

Titan ICBM powerhouse under construction by the Corps of Engineers at Denver, Colorado, in late 1959.

Operation Blue Jay

One of the more challenging assignments given to the Corps in the post-World War II period was Operation Blue Jay, the construction of a complete and modern airfield on the bleak windswept Greenland plateau at Thule, well north of the Arctic Circle. The project, dropped on the desk of Lieutenant General Lewis Pick, Chief of Engineers, during Christmas week 1950, required molding a forbidding landscape to accommodate the needs of a sophisticated airfield. Army engineers moved millions of tons of rock and gravel, erected thousands of tons of steel and aluminum, and provided water, heat, power and all the conveniences of civilization. Moreover, the construction had to be done during the short summer period of daylight.

The reconnaissance force which flew into the area in February 1951 experienced savage blizzards, solidly frozen ground and temperatures well below zero. Meanwhile machinery was mobilized at home. Nobody was sure that ships could even reach such a remote outpost; the path across the sea was littered with the wrecks of ships which had failed. The Navy was called in to help and it supplied ice breakers, tankers, survey ships, big landing craft, salvage ships and barges. On July 15, the first of these vessels made it to Greenland, and there faced another challenge—landing the supplies. The beaches were strewn with boulders. Consequently, bulldozers and other equipment were flown in. Access roads and a dock were built. All this work required around-the-clock shifts. Before it was all over, a hundred ships had anchored off-shore, 4,000 men from all the Army technical services were assigned to the construction and 6,000 construction workers were employed to complete the airfield as quickly as possible. The result was the completion of almost all construction within 100 days. The Corps of Engineers had licked the Arctic.

Barracks under construction in Vilseck, West Germany, in 1983.

demanded massive construction support. After building bases in Greenland and Iceland to protect Atlantic shipping, the Corps moved to England, where as many as 61,000 Army engineers created the ground and air facilities required to support the invasion of France. During the same period in North Africa, the Corps built many airfields for British and American air forces and provided ports and depots to support the invasion of Italy.

In June 1944, engineers moved into Europe with the Allied invasion. Operations included the rehabilitation of ports and railroads as well as airfield and depot construction. For example, engineers cleared and reconstructed the port of Le Havre using plans developed well before the advance into France. Large construction projects also included a camp and depot at Valognes, France, that served as headquarters for logistical forces of the Communications Zone. The post included tents for 11,000 soldiers and provided 560,000 square feet of hutted office space.

After the war, the Corps maintained a large presence in Europe. Engineers restored transportation networks and other public services in Germany and Austria. In France, during the early 1950s, the Corps performed a wide array of line of communications construction, from pipelines to supply depots, in anticipation of the need to reinforce units in Germany. With American troops still in Germany, engineer construction goes on there and includes hospitals, depots, billets and offices.

The Corps also remained with the occupation forces in Japan and met all of their building requirements. When war broke out in Korea, bases in Japan provided the springboard for the movement and supply of forces deployed against the North Koreans and Chinese. In Korea itself, engineers performed

remarkable feats of road and bridge construction over extremely difficult terrain and provided ports and airfields for friendly forces. They rehabilitated water supply and sanitation systems that remain in use by the Republic of Korea, and they still provide construction support for American units stationed there.

Military construction after the Korean War expanded into numerous countries. Work continued in Europe and the Far East, but increasing Cold War tensions led to the establishment of bases elsewhere. Through the 1950s and into the 1960s, the Corps built early warning facilities and airbases in diverse locales, including Greenland, Morocco and Libya.

Following the Soviet launching of Sputnik in 1957, the United States expedited the development of its intercontinental ballistic missile (ICBM) program. As the construction agent for the Air Force, the Corps established the Corps of Engineers Ballistic Missile Construction Office (CEBMCO) in 1960. CEBMCO built development, testing, and training facilities as well as the operational launch sites for the Atlas, Titan, and Minuteman missiles. In the 1970s the Corps continued construction support for missile systems, working through the Huntsville Division on the Sentinel and Safeguard antiballistic missile programs.

During the military buildup of the 1980s, the Corps conducted very large construction programs for the Army and the Air Force. For the first half of the decade, the construction effort reached approximately a billion dollars of work a year for each service. In the largest Army construction program since World War II, the Corps built a new installation at Fort Drum, New York, for a newly organized light infantry division, the 10th Mountain. Although the division used some of the existing buildings,

the Corps constructed almost an entirely new post, including infrastructure, barracks, family housing, dining facilities, headquarters buildings, a large physical fitness complex, medical clinics, and an Army airfield. Built on a tight schedule, the almost $1 billion construction program produced a modern, well-planned installation adapted to its environment and incorporating lessons learned at other Army installations. With its enclosed shopping mall, child care center, and recreational and entertainment facilities, the installation reflected the Army's growing concern about the quality of life of its soldiers and their families. Although unique in its scope and complexity, the Fort Drum program was only one portion of the busy Army and Air Force construction programs of the Reagan administration.

With the collapse of the Soviet Union and the end of the Cold War, the military construction programs declined, but important work remained. As the armed services reduced in size, the Defense Department closed and consolidated installations in the Base Realignment and Closure (BRAC) process, necessitating construction at many bases. In addition the Defense Department launched an ambitious program to clean up environmental pollution on formerly used and existing military installations. The Corps of Engineers played a large role in that cleanup effort for the Army and the Air Force. Although new construction work declined, the Corps still supported the Army and the Air Force as they adapted their installations to new technologies and improved the living conditions of service members and their families.

103

The Corps and the Space Program

Pad 34 control room, Cape Kennedy.

Man on the moon.

Apollo launch.

With past experience in missile site construction, the Army Corps of Engineers was the logical choice of Congress and the National Aeronautics and Space Administration to oversee NASA's accelerated construction program in the early 1960s. Using the Corps also eliminated the need for NASA to establish a large temporary construction staff itself. NASA contracted with the Army engineers for small facilities as well as for major projects such as the Johnson Manned Spacecraft Center in Houston, Texas, the National Space Technology Laboratories in Pearl River County, Mississippi, and the Kennedy Space Center at Cape Canaveral, Florida.

On May 25, 1961, President John F. Kennedy declared a national goal of landing a man on the moon within the decade and returning him safely to Earth. In response, NASA began a massive construction program along the Gulf of Mexico and the Atlantic Ocean, an area called the "NASA Crescent." NASA needed a new logistics system, one that it necessarily had to construct around navigable waterways, because neither road nor rail could transport the gigantic components involved in the manned space program. Waterborne transportation was the only answer. Indeed, proximity to water was a factor in the selection of Houston for a new facility. On September 25, 1961, only three days after NASA requested the Corps'

105

Public Affairs Office, Corps of Engineers

Space shuttle facility under
construction, Vandenberg
AFB, California.

assistance, the Fort Worth District
began arranging preliminary
topographic and utility surveys of
the site of the manned spacecraft
center.

Fort Worth District's experience with incremental funding stood
NASA in good stead in the construction of the center. This method
of funding is based on the congressional tradition of appropriating
construction funds on a year-to-year
basis. That meant the district contracted for each segment of the center as a separate unit. One virtue of
this procedure was that it allowed
significant changes in construction
plans without delaying the project.
For instance, on July 17, 1962,
NASA announced that the future
Mission Control Center would be
located at the center. This decision
forced the Corps to insert an entirely new building into its master
plan for the center.

The incremental funding system
also allowed for major modifications
of facilities already under construction. This was important because
speed was essential if NASA's
goals were to be met, and the engineers and NASA had to construct
buildings at the same time that
NASA was designing the laboratories and machines they would contain. Troubles with the Space Environment Simulation Chamber
showed the value of the arrangement. The failure of the chamber
during its first vacuum test required not only its redesign but also
numerous changes in the one-third-
completed building. Incremental
funding enabled contract modifications to be made without necessitating major delays. In November 1966,
after spending some $75 million on
the 1,600-acre project, Fort Worth
District completed its work on what
came to be called the Johnson
Manned Spacecraft Center.

The Mobile District's involvement in NASA's rocket test program began with the transfer of the

Army Ballistic Missile Agency's
Development Operations Division
at the George C. Marshall Space
Flight Center at Redstone Arsenal,
Huntsville, Alabama, to NASA in
1959. NASA then established the
Michoud Assembly Facility near
New Orleans as a support facility
for the Huntsville projects. Michoud
was the assembly plant for the large
Saturn booster rockets. In the fall
of 1961, NASA established its test
facility for the rockets assembled at
Michoud on a 217-square-mile tract
at the Mississippi Test Center, later
the National Space Technology
Laboratories, accessible from
Michoud by both land and water.
Mobile District spent more than
$200 million constructing space
program facilities up to the completion of the test center in April 1966.
The center's initial mission was to
test the Apollo-Saturn V second
stage booster and to test flight
models of both the first and second
stage boosters with thrusts of 7.5
million and 1 million pounds respec-
tively. The site became NASA's
principal test facility.

Canaveral District served as
NASA's construction agent for the
John F. Kennedy Space Center,
Florida, particularly in the engineering and construction of the Apollo
Launch Complex 39 and its related
industrial area, as well as Saturn
Launch Complexes 34 and 57. Because the rocket motor assemblies
required for lunar missions were the
largest yet built, construction of the
launch facilities at Complex 39 was
on an unprecedented scale. The district and its civilian contractors for
the Apollo program designed and
built the vehicle assembly building,
a structure large enough to handle
the completion of four 363-foot
Apollo-Saturn V launch vehicles; a
launch control center; three 46-story
mobile launchers, weighing 10.5 million pounds each; a 40-story mobile
services structure to permit work
on vehicles at the launch pads; two

Vehicle Assembly Building,
Cape Kennedy.

Public Affairs Office, Corps of Engineers

transporters for moving the launchers and service structure; a crawlerway road for the transporters; two launch pads, capable of withstanding the thrust from the Saturn V engines; and their integrating communications and electronics systems The American Society of Civil Engineers recognized that work in 1966 with the selection of Complex 39 and its related facilities as the outstanding civil engineering achievement of the year.

Other Corps offices completed additional construction for NASA. For example, the New England Division selected the site for and supervised the construction of the Electronics Research Center in Cambridge, Massachusetts, in the late 1960s. That facility is now the Transportation Systems Center. In supervising a $1 billion NASA construction effort, Corps offices in all parts of the country made major contributions to the national space effort.

Saturn 4B launching
Apollo.

Work for Other Nations

Reconstruction at Piraeus Harbor, Greece, February 1948.

Office of History, Corps of Engineers

George C. Marshall.

U.S. Army

Public Affairs Office, Corps of Engineers

Precast plant, King Khalid Military City, Al Batin, Saudi Arabia.

Shortly after World War II, the Corps of Engineers became involved in massive foreign assistance programs sponsored by the United States. These efforts responded to two closely connected results of the war. In the first place, much of Europe was a shambles, characterized in many instances by physical devastation and political instability. These conditions made the continent vulnerable to the apparently expansive goals of the Soviet Union. As a result, in 1947 Congress approved Secretary of State George C. Marshall's plan to provide financial support for reconstruction programs developed by participating European nations and separate aid packages for Greece and Turkey, which appeared particularly vulnerable to subversion or aggression.

The 1951 Mutual Security Act extended the foreign assistance program to other portions of the globe. This law was passed in a period of growing international tension, marked by the Berlin blockade, the Communist success in China and the Korean War. The purpose of the legislation was maintenance of the national security and promotion of U.S. foreign policy through military, economic and technical assistance to strengthen friendly nations. This remains the fundamental goal of the program. The act consolidated a variety of efforts, including the Military Assistance Program, authorized in 1949 by the Mutual Defense Assistance Act, through which the United States offered help to allies in establishing defenses against external aggression and internal violence. The Mutual Security Act also included the program of technical assistance first articulated as Point Four of President Truman's 1949 inaugural address. Finally, the new law replaced the various economic aid programs with comprehensive loan and grant provisions.

The current basic law, the Foreign Assistance Act of 1961, established the Agency for International Development (AID) within the State Department to administer the major economic aid programs. More significantly for later Corps of Engineers activities, section 607 provided for the furnishing of services and commodities to foreign

109

Dredging on the Suez Canal.

countries on a reimbursable basis. In the mid-1960s, this became the basis for major engineering programs.

Within the context of these laws, foreign assistance programs evolved to meet changing perceptions of the world situation and American interests. In the first period, from 1947 to 1952, economic aid predominated. During the Eisenhower years, from 1953 through 1960, most of the assistance from the United States was military. Then, in the decade that followed, an equilibrium was reached between economic assistance and military programs, including sales.

Other important trends shaped the role of the Corps in foreign programs. The emphasis on Europe during the early years after World War II, including Korean War bases in Middle Eastern and North African countries close to Europe, changed when the situation there stabilized. In the mid-1950s, the European share of American support dwindled to almost nothing, and the focus shifted to the Far East, South Asia and the Middle East. This trend coincided with another noteworthy tendency. During 1948-1952, most aid was in the form of grants. In fact, 90 percent of American help took the form of outright gifts. By the mid-1960s, 60 percent of economic aid was by loan.

The Corps of Engineers' contributions to these foreign programs took place in this context of evolving emphasis. Thus, during the immediate post-war years when American foreign policy and assistance programs emphasized Europe and particularly Greece and Turkey, the Corps was extremely active in these two nations. In Turkey, the Corps concentrated on construction of military facilities for Turkish and American armed forces. In Greece, after the State Department came to

the Corps for technical expertise, the Corps restored a badly mauled transportation and communication network. The Grecian District, which was established in Athens in July 1947, cleared the Corinth Canal, restored the port of Piraeus, and built or repaired more than 3,000 kilometers of roads.

The Corps' operations in Greece established several major precedents. First was the organization of an engineer district to administer and supervise large-scale civil works in a foreign country. Second was the provision of technical assistance in conjunction with economic aid. Third, the practice of training indigenous contractors and artisans to perform as much of the actual work as possible began in Greece. And, fourth, the commitment to helping a friendly nation to help itself, which was manifested in projects aimed at restoring the Greek economy, became a standard feature of Corps projects.

During the 1950s, the Military Assistance Program dominated American overseas efforts. This program was one of two major Department of Defense foreign activities in which the Corps participated. First and most important was the maintenance and support of American forces in other lands. The other, the Military Assistance Program through which the United States aided the military forces of other nations, was directed largely toward supporting allies on the periphery of the Soviet Union and near the People's Republic of China.

In the period 1950-1964, this program dispensed assistance valued at more than $350 million. Iran, which was the largest single recipient, and four other nations—Pakistan, Turkey, Taiwan and Korea—received nearly all of the military assistance money. The projects carried out in Pakistan by the Trans-East District of the Mediterranean Division illustrate the nature of the

work performed. In a massive modernization program for the Pakistani armed forces, the Corps built cantonments, airfields, wharves and marine railways.

While heavily involved in these efforts, the Corps also worked in programs of economic assistance. Projects intended to buttress a recipient nation's economy were administered by the AID and predecessor agencies. Corps participation in economic development programs actually predated the establishment of any of these agencies. As early as 1946, the Corps of Engineers worked with numerous Latin American governments to establish national cartographic programs. These efforts were ultimately intended to provide the basis for resource inventories of participating nations. After 1953, when the Department of State took over this program, the Corps continued to contribute to its success. Engineer personnel worked in 22 countries, developing programs, rendering procurement assistance, and administering contracts.

In the late 1950s the Corps began to undertake large projects within the economic assistance program. Between 1950 and 1964 the Corps produced major engineering studies for 17 different countries. These surveys dealt with beach erosion problems, river hydraulics, transportation networks and entire public works programs. Engineer personnel also examined the feasibility of various port and highway projects. The engineers also became involved in actual construction in eight countries. The major projects included airports, highway systems and ports. In the six years from 1959 through 1964, these efforts resulted in expenditures of $109.5 million.

The Corps' work on these studies and construction projects reflected new directions in the overall program administered by the AID.

Enlisted quarters, King Khalid Military City.

In the years just prior to 1965, the focus was on long-term projects that supported broad economic development. In this framework engineering and construction loomed large and the Corps, with its unique capability to plan, organize and execute major building programs, made major contributions.

During the mid-1960s several developments led to changes in the Corps' role in foreign programs. AID changed its emphasis from major construction efforts aimed at improving economic infrastructures to more immediate needs for improvement of food supplies, public health and education. Moreover, the agency turned more to private engineering and architectural firms for support in this area. In so doing the agency cited for justification the provisions of section 601 of the Foreign Assistance Act of 1961, which encouraged maximum utilization of private resources instead of other government agencies.

The buildup of American armed forces in Vietnam also redirected the Corps' foreign operations. The maintenance and support of American forces in Southeast Asia took an ever-increasing portion of the Corps' resources. Moreover, Vietnam absorbed a growing percentage of the foreign aid budget, leaving less money for major projects in

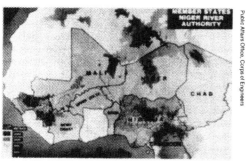

1980 saw Corps support for navigation and planning in the Niger basin.

Port of Owendo, Gabon, West Central Africa, site of Corps studies for AID.

111

Israeli airbase under construction.

other parts of the world. As AID turned its attention to Vietnam and Southeast Asia, it became involved in major geodetic and cartographic enterprises. The Corps of Engineers, with expertise already employed in a number of other nations, contributed again to resource inventory projects and the production of maps required for the land reform program of the government of South Vietnam. Thus, while the Corps' involvement in major construction projects dropped off, it still participated in other aspects of AID's work.

Even before these developments changed the character of Corps overseas projects, another major factor entered the picture. This was the beginning of Corps involvement in reimbursable programs funded by recipient nations instead of by United States loans and grants. Authorized by section 607 of the Foreign Assistance Act, these projects were based on bilateral agreement between the United States and nations that sought Corps technical expertise in development programs. The first of these was funded by the government of Saudi Arabia in 1963. There the Corps engaged in a large number of construction projects, including a variety of facilities for the Saudi Arabian armed forces and civil projects such as construction of radio and television communications installations.

In the late 1960s and early 1970s, the number of reimbursable programs grew. In addition to the ongoing work in Saudi Arabia, where over $5 billion in construction has been completed, projects started in several other countries, among them Iran, Jordan, Kuwait and Libya. The Corps' effort in these nations improved the American balance of payments and provided valuable experience for engineer personnel while sharing the Corps' technical and professional expertise.

While managing reimbursable long-term projects, the Corps met more pressing requirements in the Middle East. In accordance with the Camp David agreement, the Corps built two airbases for Israel as replacements for those evacuated during the withdrawal from the Sinai. Finished in 1982, only three years after the start of construction, the bases cost about $1 billion, over three-fourths of which was an American grant. Meanwhile, the Corps also constructed Sinai base camps for the Multinational Force and Observers who patrol the demilitarized zone between Egypt and Israel.

Although the reimbursable programs of recent years have been less extensive than the massive Saudi Arabian and Israeli air base ones, they continue to be an important Corps mission as the agency explores the role it can play in "nation building" around the world. The wide variety of studies and projects to assist other nations included technical assistance to the African nation of Gabon in improving its ports, geological and hydrological studies of the Niger River basin in Africa, technical advice on water resources development to the People's Republic of China, disaster relief in Bangladesh after devastating floods in 1991, and construction of hydropower facilities in the Federated States of Micronesia. Whatever the scope of the project, the Corps seeks, as it has since the end of World War II, to assist other nations in improving their infrastructures, to share American technical know-how, and to help other coun-

tries develop their own capabilities for nation building. From massive construction programs like the one in Saudi Arabia to feasibility studies like the one for the port of Asau in Western Samoa, the Corps has developed the ability to assist other nations in a wide variety of engineering and construction management activities.

Dhahran Airport, Saudi Arabia.

Housing courtyard,
King Abdul Aziz Military
Academy.

Strengthening the Free World: Rehabilitation in Greece 1947-49

The advantages of having a military-civilian engineer organization in being were demonstrated when the United States decided to help Greece recover from the devastation of war.

Soon after the end of World War II, Greece was torn by a civil war between Communist guerrillas and government troops. President Truman and Congress believed it was in the national interest to prevent a Communist takeover. To strengthen the anti-Communist forces, a program of economic aid to Greece was developed under the auspices of the State Department. A Greece on the road to economic recovery would be less likely to fall to Communism.

President Harry S. Truman appointed Dwight P. Griswold, a former governor of Nebraska, as the administrator of the recovery program. Soon after his arrival in Greece in July 1947, Griswold reported on the extensive devastation he found. The State Department decided that the reconstruction and rehabilitation of roads, railroads, bridges, ports and the Corinth Canal, one of the main Greek waterways, were of primary importance. Once the country's transportation system was restored and the ports were in operable condition, economic recovery would be more rapid.

The State Department received some 100 letters from construction firms interested in doing the work. The department was, however, unfamiliar with doing construction and letting contracts and had no organization to do the job. It sent representatives a number of times to the Office of the Chief of Engineers to get information regarding such matters as the selection of contractors, the types of contracts that could be used and the amount of the fee to be paid. The State Department concluded it would be unable to do the work because it did not have the know-how in dealing with contractors and had no organization to put into Greece. It asked the engineers, who had a far-flung civil works construction organization, to do the work. The Secretary of State requested the Secretary of War

to assume responsibility for the job. Assigned to the Corps of Engineers in late July 1947, it was scheduled to be completed within a year.

The engineers set up the Grecian District with headquarters in Athens, with personnel to be largely drawn from divisions and districts, and entered into agreements with a number of contractors who formed joint ventures. In mid-August, Colonel David W. Griffiths, the new district engineer, some of his civilian employees and some of the contractors' employees arrived in Athens. Actual reconstruction began in mid-September with the clearing away of debris from the harbor of Piraeus, the port of Athens. Soon work was under way on the reconstruction of other ports, the reconstruction of wrecked railroad bridges and tunnels and on the upgrading of highways, which had deteriorated badly. The Corinth Canal was cleared of debris. Soon after arriving in Greece, Colonel Griffiths was given the additional duty of upgrading a number of airfields. All of this work had to be done rapidly and efficiently. As the Secretary of War wrote, "The War Department is on continual exhibition to the President, the Congress, the State Department and to Greece . . . and other interested nations." Colonel George W. Marvin, the chief engineer of the U.S. Army Group advising the Greek Army in its fight against the guerrillas, helped Colonel Griffiths by obtaining Greek Army units to provide security for men working on District projects.

The Corps reconstructed about 900 miles of highway, rebuilt three major ports, restored railroad bridges and tunnels totalling some two miles, and upgraded 10 airfields. The Corinth Canal was reopened after about 1 million cubic yards of earth and debris had been removed. Actual construction time was about a year and a half; the overrun resulted mainly from guerrilla attacks, unusually severe winter weather, and delays in getting supplies. Once again, the engineer military-civil organization made possible the efficient accomplishment of a mission.

113

Changing Military Responsibilities and Relationships

During World War II, the Office of the Chief of Engineers and its subordinate activities exercised a broad range of military responsibilities. The Corps trained engineer officers and enlisted men, primarily at Fort Belvoir, Virginia, home of the Army's Engineer School since 1919, and at Fort Leonard Wood, Missouri, where an Engineer Replacement Training Center opened in 1941. It developed the tables of organization and equipment that structured Army engineer units, wrote the technical manuals that explained the use of engineer equipment, and prepared the field manuals that detailed military engineering tactics and doctrine. The Corps of Engineers determined the Army's engineer equipment requirements, purchased the items needed, and distributed them, while supervising the efforts of the Engineer Board to develop new and improved equipment. It selected engineer officers for assignment to troop units, schools, and civil works. The Corps supervised all Army map making. Finally, it met the huge military construction and real estate needs of a rapidly expanding Army.

These functions, with the exception of general military construction and Army real estate, were traditional Corps missions that the Corps pursued during the war in vastly expanded form. Three months after the attack on Pearl Harbor, however, its position within the War Department changed as the Corps and other Army technical and administrative services were placed under the Services of Supply, one of three major components into which the War Department was then divided. General Brehon Somervell, himself an engineer officer, commanded this organization throughout the war, although its title changed in 1943 to Army Service Forces.

When the Army Service Forces headquarters was dissolved in 1946, the Chief of Engineers and the chiefs of the Army's other technical services returned briefly to the direct supervision of the Army Chief of Staff. The Director of Logistics, however, inherited the general supervision of the technical services in 1948, and the Deputy Chief of Staff for Logistics obtained more effective oversight of their work in 1954. The Under Secretary of the Army (during 1950-1953) and Assistant Secretaries of the Army for Materiel; Financial Management; Civil-Military Affairs; and Manpower, Personnel, and Reserve Forces (during the Eisenhower administration) successively provided civilian direction for the Corps' military construction, housing, and real property functions.

For a decade and a half after World War II, the Army Corps of Engineers undertook the same broad range of functions it had exercised during the war. It even retained its role as engineering and construction agent for the U.S. Air Force after that service became independent of the Army in 1947. In 1954 the Corps became responsible for the Army's nuclear reactor program. It created the Army Engineer Reactors Group, which in 1957 completed, in conjunction with the Atomic Energy Commission, the nation's first military nuclear power plant built primarily to generate electricity. Other nuclear plants followed, including a floating power plant and field reactors producing both steam heat and electricity.

A sand grid confinement system designed by the Waterways Experiment Station to construct solid military roads across beach or desert sands.

Waterways Experiment Station

115

Enriched uranium nuclear power reactor erected at Fort Belvoir, Virginia, in 1955-1957 by the Army Engineer Reactors Group and the Atomic Energy Commission. The Army's first nuclear power reactor, this facility was decommissioned in 1973.

Research Laboratories

The Corps' laboratories prospered in the postwar years.

The Engineer Research and Development Laboratories at Fort Belvoir, successor to the Engineer Board, continued its work in developing new and improved bridging, road-construction, camouflage, demolition, mapping, and mechanical equipment. A Nuclear Power Branch was added to the laboratory to engage in research and development in the nuclear power field.

The Waterways Experiment Station, established by the Corps and its Mississippi River Commission in 1929 at Vicksburg, Mississippi, as a hydraulics laboratory, had entered the field of military research and development during World War II. It then helped to develop the pierced-steel plank and prefabricated bituminous surface used in U.S. Army airfield construction. Placed under the direct supervision of the Chief of Engineers in 1949, the Waterways Experiment Station after the war developed flexible pavements for runways designed for new, heavy B-52 bombers, and it examined, through chemical simulation, the blast effects of nuclear detonations in an effort to produce hardened struc-

The Waterways Experiment Station around 1940, shortly before World War II refocused much of the laboratory's attention on military requirements.

Part of the one-mile sand grid demonstration road constructed at a Joint Logistics over-the-shore test at Fort Story, Virginia.

116

The Cold Regions Research and Engineering Laboratory, Hanover, New Hampshire.

tures capable of withstanding such attack.

Responding to increased Army emphasis on Arctic defenses, the Corps of Engineers during and after the war established laboratories at Wilmette, Illinois, and Boston, Massachusetts, to study the impact of cold climates on military operations. These Corps laboratories conducted research and experimentation on materials and techniques suitable for construction in areas of snow, ice, and permafrost. Their efforts aided the development of the Distant Early Warning (DEW) Line Radar System in Greenland, northern Canada, and Alaska and of American airfields and bases in that region. The laboratories consolidated in 1961 to form the Cold Regions Research and Engineering Laboratory at Hanover, New Hampshire.

Reorganized Army

Seeking to streamline the Army's structure, Secretary of Defense Robert McNamara in 1962 implemented the most substantial reorganization of the Army in the post-World War II era. All of the Army's technical service chiefs, except for the Chief of Engineers and the Surgeon General, were eliminated, and three newly created functional commands took important responsibilities from the Chief of Engineers. The Army Combat Developments Command assumed responsibility for engineer training and military doctrine. The Office of Personnel Operations took over the career management of engineer officers. The Army Materiel Command assumed engineer supply and equipment development functions.

Overseeing the development, purchase, and supply of a wide range of Army weapons and equipment, the Army Materiel Command created a number of

A Distant Early Warning Line station on the Greenland ice cap.

major subordinate commands to which it assigned responsibility for specific types of items. The Army Mobility Command (1962-1967) and its successor, the Army Mobility Equipment Command, took over the supply of most military engineering equipment and the supervision of the Engineering Research and Development Laboratories at Fort Belvoir, which became the Army Mobility Equipment Research and Development Center. The two commanders of the Army Mobility Command, Major Generals Alden Sibley and William Lapsley, were both engineer officers, and Sibley moved to the Mobility Command directly from his duties as the last Deputy Chief of Engineers for Military Operations. This eased the transition in engineer supply matters.

Major General William Gribble, later Chief of Engineers, served as

Construction in early 1989 on the Army Engineer School, Fort Leonard Wood, Missouri, under the direction of the U.S. Army Engineer District, Kansas City.

Dormitory built in 1965 for U.S. Air Force personnel at San Vito dei Normanni in southern Italy.

the Army Materiel Command's Director of Research and Development in 1964-1966, and Major General Richard Free, another engineer officer, held that position from 1967-1969. These were important years for the development of new engineer materiel used to support American forces in Vietnam. Aided by renewed experimentation in airfield mats and membranes at the Waterways Experiment Station, the Materiel Command developed the prefabricated, neoprene-coated nylon membrane known as the T-17 membrane, used on airfields in Vietnam; new aluminum and steel landing mats; and peneprime, a high penetration asphalt that met dust-control needs in Vietnam. The Chief of Engineers remained the senior engineer adviser to the Army Chief of Staff, and his advice was sought and implemented on such decisions as the selection of the D-7 dozer as the standard bulldozer in Vietnam, in preference to the newer but less easily transported D-8 model.

Despite its loss of important training, personnel, and materiel supply responsibilities in 1962, the Office of the Chief of Engineers continued to supervise the engineering, construction, and real estate services required by the Army, Air Force, and National Aeronautics and Space Administration. The Chief's office also continued to formulate Army policies governing the maintenance and repair of Army housing and other real property and the operation of the utilities on Army installations, as it had since World War II. Army facilities

Houses constructed at Ben Guerin, Morocco.

engineers implemented these policies under the supervision of installation commanders. The Chief of Engineers, however, lost control of funding in the repairs and utilities sphere in 1958. The Chief of Engineers' work in all of these fields remained under the general staff supervision of the Deputy Chief of Staff for Logistics, while the Assistant Secretary of the Army for Installations and Logistics in 1961 assumed civilian oversight of all of these functions.

In addition, the Office of the Chief of Engineers continued to supervise Army mapping, geodesy, and military geographic intelligence services, maintaining the Defense Department's worldwide map library as it had since 1939. Beginning in 1963 and 1964, it exercised its topographic responsibilities under the program direction of the Assistant Secretary of the Army for Research and Development and the Army Staff direction of the Assistant Chief of Staff for Intelligence.

While the Engineer Research and Development Laboratories was placed under the Army Materiel Command in 1962, its former topographic and nuclear power development functions remained Corps of Engineers responsibilities. With the field of military mapping research expanding rapidly at the dawn of the satellite era, the Chief of Engineers in 1960 had transferred this function from the Engineer Research and Development Laboratories to the newly created Engineer Geodesy, Intelligence, and Mapping Research and Development Agency. The reorganization of 1962 left that agency part of the Corps of Engineers. The agency was renamed the Engineer Topographic Laboratories in 1967.

The Defense Department consolidated the topographic work of the different military services in 1972, however, and the U.S. Army Topographic Command, whose director had reported to the Chief of Engineers, was absorbed into the new Defense Mapping Agency. The Chief of Engineers again retained responsibility for Army topographic research and development. The Engineer Topographic Laboratories, located at Fort Belvoir, Virginia, developed during the 1960s and 1970s automated equipment for producing topographic maps from aerial photographs and improved systems of Army field map production. In the 1980s they developed systems to convert terrain data into digital form and used computer graphics to offer Army commanders access to this data in a variety of easily interpreted formats. The Corps renamed the topographic laboratories as the Topographic Engineering Center in 1991.

The Army Engineer Reactors Group, renamed in 1971 the Army Engineer Power Group, retained the Corps' responsibility for Army nuclear power development after the 1962 reorganization. In May 1962 the Corps created the Army Engineer Nuclear Cratering Group at Livermore, California, to study, in cooperation with the Atomic Energy Commission, the feasibility of nuclear methods of excavation. Although officials considered using nuclear devices in the construction of a proposed sea-level canal across Central America and in several civil works projects in the United States, no feasible occasion was found to employ this concept. The Corps disbanded the Nuclear Cratering Group in 1971.

The Cold Regions Research and Engineering Laboratory was transferred to the Army Materiel Command in 1962, but because of continuing Corps of Engineers requirements for arctic construction research, the Materiel Command approved its return to the Corps of Engineers in 1969.

The autonomous land vehicle, a test robotic vehicle developed by the U.S. Army Engineer Topographic Laboratories.

Biaxial shock test machine designed by the U.S. Army Construction Engineering Research Laboratory to test both horizontal and vertical structural strength.

A portable weld quality monitor developed for field quality assurance by the U.S. Army Construction Engineering Research Laboratory.

After the transfer of the Engineer Research and Development Laboratories to the Army Materiel Command, the Chief of Engineers sought the creation of a new facility to conduct basic research into questions of construction materials and design, housing habitability and maintenance, and energy and utility systems. As the Ohio River Division's Construction Engineering Laboratory at Cincinnati had begun significant work in this sphere, the Corps with the approval of the Army secretariat expanded that facility into a new Construction Engineering Research Laboratory. The new laboratory opened at Cincinnati in 1968 and moved the following year to its present location at Champaign, Illinois, where it occupied facilities leased from the University of Illinois. This newest Corps laboratory developed a fibrous reinforced concrete used both in airfield runways and in some civil works projects, a portable instrument to test welding quality, and a centralized facility to control pollutants where Army vehicles are washed.

Engineer Troop Units

After World War II, Army engineer troops were organized primarily into engineer combat and construction battalions, supplemented by topographic battalions and various specialized engineer companies. The combat battalions

Centralized wash facility for Army equipment developed by the U.S. Army Construction Engineering Research Laboratory.

were designed to provide the engineering capabilities required by frontline forces, and their men were trained and equipped to fight as infantry if necessary. Engineer construction battalions had heavier equipment suited for the more permanent construction typically required to the rear of combat zones, and its members were not expected to fight as infantry. Lieutenant General Walter Wilson, the Chief of Engineers, proposed in 1962 to eliminate the engineer construction battalion and create a single, standardized engineer combat battalion that could be aided, when required for heavier work, by a construction equipment company. The Combat Developments Command studied Wilson's proposal but concluded that the construction battalion would be essential in the event of a lengthy war. Subsequent events in Vietnam supported this conclusion, for engineer construction battalions there played a leading role in the construction of Army installations and an ambitious highway development program.

The Chief of Engineers regained Army Staff responsibility for the development of Army engineer units in 1969, and a reevaluation of the proper role of the engineer construction battalion soon ensued. The Engineer Strategic Studies Group, a broadly chartered studies and analysis activity reporting to the Chief of Engineers, proposed in 1974 that the engineer construction battalion be reorganized and its firepower augmented so that it, too, would be prepared to assume a full combat role. In the contemporary climate of congressional concern over the military's proportion of combat and support forces, frequently termed the "tooth-to-tail ratio," the Army then accepted this proposal, and engineer construction battalions at home and abroad were reorganized in 1975 as engineer combat (heavy) battalions. As part of the reorganization, the units were provided additional antitank weapons, grenade launchers, radios, and demolition equipment, and their men were given additional combat training. The conversion of the engineer construction battalions in Europe contributed significantly to the reduction of the Army's support forces there mandated by the Defense Appropriation Authorization Act for 1975. In that same year, the Army again included the Corps of Engineers among the Army's combat arms branches, while retaining it among its combat support arms and its services.

Army Facilities Programs

The Corps substantially increased its responsibility over the Army's military construction and family housing programs in 1974. Prior to that time the Deputy Chief of Staff for Logistics formulated Army budget planning and set basic policies for these facilities programs, which the Corps then executed. The Deputy Chief of Staff for Logistics exercised these functions through his Director of Installations, as he and his predecessors had done since 1954. As part of a larger transfer of Army Staff responsibilities to operating elements, the Army in 1974 placed the Director of Installations, Major General Kenneth Cooper, together with his staff and his

Construction Engineering Research Laboratory

121

Cast iron building at Watervliet Arsenal, New York, erected in 1859 by Architectural Iron Works of New York. Today, it houses an Army museum. Named a National Historic Landmark by the Secretary of the Interior, it is the only totally iron building that survives in the United States.

program development responsibilities, under the Chief of Engineers. General Cooper became Assistant Chief of Engineers. In the same year the Corps added facilities engineering technical assistance and fossil-fuel energy consulting to the then dwindling Army nuclear power responsibilities of the Army Engineer Power Group, and it renamed this very changed group the Facilities Engineering Support Agency.

Environmental Responsibilities

The Army Chief of Staff in 1966 assigned the Chief of Engineers supervision over the engineering aspects of the Army's emerging program to protect the environment and abate pollution in the construction and operation of its military facilities. He instructed the Surgeon General and the Chief of Engineers to work together to develop Army pollution abatement programs. In 1971 the Deputy Chief of Staff for Logistics assumed primary Army Staff responsibility for directing the Army's environmental preservation and improvement activities, exclusive of the civil works arena. His Director of Installations created an Environmental Office in that year to undertake this responsibility. The Chief of Engineers continued to supervise the engineering portion of the program.

When the Director of Installations became the Assistant Chief of Engineers in 1974, the Corps of Engineers added the direction of Army environmental efforts related to military sites to those involving civil works projects. This mission came to include supervising the Army's water pollution abatement and solid waste management programs, issuing policies for monitoring and controlling air pollutants emitted by Army facilities and

The century-old Officers Club at Fort Totten New York, a structure listed on the National Register of Historic Places.

A bulldozer removing contaminated soil at Rocky Mountain Arsenal, Colorado, a former chemical weapons production facility located ten miles northeast of Denver.

vehicles, and drafting regulations to govern the Army's management of hazardous and toxic materials, its noise abatement efforts, and its responses to any Army-caused oil spills. The Corps also assumed responsibility in 1974 for an Army program to preserve buildings of historic or architectural significance and noteworthy archaeological sites on Army properties. The Office of the Assistant Secretary of the Army for Civil Works assumed civilian direction of the Army's military environmental program upon the office's establishment in 1975. The Army shifted this oversight function to the office of the assistant secretary of the Army responsible for installations and logistics in 1978.

The creation of the Defense Environmental Restoration Program, first funded by a 1983 act, has led to a noteworthy enlargement of the Corps' environmental work relating to military installations. The three services had earlier initiated efforts to remove hazardous materials from their active installations. The new program added hazardous waste disposal from former military sites and the removal of unsafe buildings, ordnance, and other debris from both active and former military sites. The Corps of Engineers, which had already begun providing engineering assistance to the Environmental Protection Agency in its direction of civilian toxic waste removal under the Superfund program enacted in 1980, assumed program management in 1984 of the environmental restoration program for all former military sites, irrespective of service. The Deputy for Environmental Policy in the Office of the Deputy Assistant Secretary of Defense for Installations selected sites for cleanup, after considering the recommendations of the Office of the Chief of Engineers. The defense official's

position was raised to Deputy Assistant Secretary of Defense, Environment, in 1986. The U.S. Army Toxic and Hazardous Materials Agency, created in 1978 at Aberdeen, Maryland, as a subordinate activity of the Army Materiel Command, maintained operational control of the expanded environmental restoration program on active Army installations, but it too relied on the Corps of Engineers for most of its design and construction work. The Corps has provided similar assistance in the cleanup of many active Air Force installations. In 1988 the Army placed the Toxic and Hazardous Materials Agency under the Chief of Engineers, consolidating Army environmental responsibilities under a single head.

Army Facilities Maintenance

The Corps of Engineers increased its involvement in maintaining and repairing Army housing and other facilities at the same time as it broadened its environmental responsibilities. A study panel headed by Engineer Lieutenant General Lawrence Lincoln in

The award-winning volatilization system that in one year removed more than 100,000 pounds of dangerous organic compounds, such as the degreasing agent trichloroethylene, which contaminated groundwater around the Twin Cities Army Ammunition Plant, Minnesota.

1968 urged the Army to encourage installation facilities engineers to turn to Corps of Engineers districts and divisions for engineering support by funding a portion of that work. The Army agreed to set aside a modest fund for Corps installation support, invited commanders to turn to the Corps for additional maintenance and repair work on a reimbursable basis, and took other actions recommended by the Lincoln panel to strengthen facilities engineering.

When the administration of President Jimmy Carter proposed management consolidation and increased reliance on private-sector contracting in the maintenance of Army facilities, the Corps of Engineers undertook several new studies in this sphere. A panel headed by Brigadier General Donald Weinert reviewed Army facilities engineering in the context of the era's heightened emphasis on master planning, energy conservation, worker safety, and environmental protection. The group observed in 1978 that the Corps' resources were still often neglected in the facilities maintenance sphere, despite the Army's implementation of most of the Lincoln panel's recommendations. A subsequent engineer planning group headed by Colonel Charles Blalock proposed incorporating installation facilities engineers into the Corps' district organization, aiding them with the Corps' substantial experience in contracting and giving them a full range of local engineering responsibilities. Although the Army did not accept the offer of Lieutenant General John W. Morris, Chief of Engineers, to assume such broad installation engineering responsibilities, it did approve the plan, elaborated by the Engineer Studies Center (formerly the Engineer Strategic Studies Group), to centralize Army facilities maintenance work

in the Military District of Washington under a single engineer manager. The Corps of Engineers in 1980 created the Engineer Activity, Capital Area, at Fort Myer, Virginia, to exercise that function.

While installation commanders retained responsibility for maintenance work on Army posts, their facilities engineers turned increasingly to Corps districts and divisions for assistance in prosecuting the Reagan administration's substantial effort to reduce the backlog of Army repair and maintenance work. Streamlining its procedures in this sphere, the Corps of the Engineers saw its reimbursable instal-

lation support work grow from $130 million in 1980 to $620 million in 1986. Effective Corps support in this sphere was enhanced by new administrative reforms proposed by internal reviews made in 1985 and 1988, the former by a panel headed by North Central Division Engineer Brigadier General Jerome Hilmes and the latter by the Office of the Engineer Inspector General, Colonel Dennis Bulger.

A Major Command

Witnessing a decline in support for large, new water resources projects in the late 1970s, Chief of

Contract workmen install utilities in new Army Engineer School, Fort Leonard Wood, Missouri.

Missouri River Division

Engineers Morris attempted to strengthen his office's ties to the Army as a whole. This effort led to the designation in 1979 of the Corps of Engineers—comprising the Office of the Chief of Engineers, together with the divisions, districts, laboratories, and other agencies subordinate to the Chief of Engineers—as an Army major command. This status gave the Corps a position comparable to other leading specialized Army commands, including the Training and Doctrine Command, Materiel Command, Communications Command and Health Services Command and the Army components of unified geographic commands, such as U.S. Army, Europe. The Chief of Engineers' ties to the Army were strengthened further in 1986 when he was named Chief of the Corps of Engineers Regiment, a ceremonial institution through which all engineer soldiers, officers and units would participate in the new U.S. Army Regimental System. The Chief of Engineers' assumption of this position gave symbolic recognition to his office's long history of leadership among the Army's military engineers.

The Goldwater-Nichols Department of Defense Reorganization Act of 1986 obliged the Army to distinguish clearly between the small group of personnel who continued to serve the Chief of Engineers in his capacity as an Army Staff officer, who advised the Chief of Staff, and the larger number who worked for him as commander of the U.S. Army Corps of Engineers, the engineering and construction organiza-

tion. The act also mandated personnel reductions that had an impact on the Office of the Chief of Engineers as an Army Staff office. Responding to both the Army Staff personnel limitations and his own view of current management requirements, the Chief of Engineers, Lieutenant General E. R. Heiberg III, ordered the consolidation into a new Corps of Engineers organization of the Facilities Engineering Support Agency and the technical support activities of the Assistant Chief of Engineers in the fields of facilities engineering and housing management. The new organization, called the U.S. Army Engineering and Housing Support Center, was established in 1987 at Fort Belvoir, Virginia. Its creation left Army program development responsibilities in the facilities and housing spheres in a leaner Office of the Assistant Chief of Engineers, now distinctly an Army Staff organization. The Army Environmental Office became an Army Staff support agency, which also reported to the Assistant Chief of Engineers. The new Engineering and Housing Support Center assumed responsibility for providing engineering support and technical policy interpretation in the facilities and housing spheres to Army forces worldwide.

As the Army turned more of its attention to its domestic installations in the aftermath of the Cold War, Acting Secretary of the Army John Shannon in 1993 gave broad authority over planning, programming, and general support for Army bases, facilities, and environmental restoration efforts to a new

Assistant Chief of Staff for Installations Management. This new Army Staff officer assumed most of the responsibilities of the Assistant Chief of Engineers, whose office was abolished. The Army Environmental Office; the Army Environmental Center, as the U.S. Army Toxic and Hazardous Materials Agency had been renamed; and elements of the Engineering and Housing Support Center involved in policy were also placed under the new assistant chief of staff. General officers who had previously reported to the Chief of Engineers became the first Directors of Environmental Programs and of Facilities and Housing for the Assistant Chief of Staff for Installations Management. The military engineering and topography functions that had been overseen by the Assistant Chief of Engineers, however, remained Army Staff responsibilities of the Chief of Engineers. They were henceforth exercised by the newly established Office of the Chief of Engineers (Pentagon). The Engineering and Housing Support Center was renamed the U.S. Army Center for Public Works. Remaining under the Chief of Engineers, it has continued to provide technical support to installation commanders. Overall, the Corps of Engineers retained its design and construction missions, including the execution of a large and expanding program for the cleanup of hazardous materials at current Army and Air Force installations and former defense sites.

Ninety-ninth Congress of the United States of America

AT THE SECOND SESSION

Begun and held at the City of Washington on Tuesday, the twenty-first day of January, one thousand nine hundred and eighty-six

An Act

To provide for the conservation and development of water and related resources and the improvement and rehabilitation of the Nation's water resources infrastructure.

Be it enacted by the Senate and House of Representatives of the United States of America in Congress assembled,

SECTION 1. SHORT TITLE AND TABLE OF CONTENTS.

(a) SHORT TITLE.—This Act may be cited as the "Water Resources Development Act of 1986".

(b) TABLE OF CONTENTS.—

Title I—Cost Sharing
Title II—Harbor Development
Title III—Inland Waterway Transportation System
Title IV—Flood Control
Title V—Shoreline Protection
Title VI—Water Resources Conservation and Development
Title VII—Water Resources Studies
Title VIII—Project Modifications
Title IX—General Provisions
Title X—Project Deauthorizations
Title XI—Miscellaneous Programs and Projects
Title XII—Dam Safety
Title XIII—Namings
Title XIV—Revenue Provisions

SEC. 2. DEFINITION OF SECRETARY.

For purposes of this Act, the term "Secretary" means the Secretary of the Army.

TITLE I—COST SHARING

SEC. 101. HARBORS.—

(a) CONSTRUCTION.—

(1) PAYMENTS DURING CONSTRUCTION.—The non-Federal interests for a navigation project for a harbor or inland harbor, or any separable element thereof, on which a contract for physical construction has not been awarded before the date of enactment of this Act shall pay, during the period of construction of the project, the following costs associated with general navigation features:

(A) 10 percent of the cost of construction of the portion of the project which has a depth not in excess of 20 feet; plus

(B) 25 percent of the cost of construction of the portion of the project which has a depth in excess of 20 feet but not in excess of 45 feet; plus

(C) 50 percent of the cost of construction of the portion of the project which has a depth in excess of 45 feet.

(2) ADDITIONAL 10 PERCENT PAYMENT OVER 30 YEARS.—The non-Federal interests for a project to which paragraph (1) applies shall pay an additional 10 percent of the cost of the general navigation features of the project in cash over a period

---

H. R. 6—192

appropriate Federal agencies, shall conduct a study to determine the impact of the port use tax imposed under section 4461(a) of the Internal Revenue Code of 1954 on potential diversions of cargo from particular United States ports to any port in a country contiguous to the United States. The report of the study shall be submitted to the Ways and Means Committee of the House of Representatives and the Committee on Finance of the United States Senate not later than 1 year from the date of the enactment of this Act.

REVIEW.—The Secretary of the Treasury may, at any time, review and revise the findings of the study conducted pursuant to subsection (a) with respect to any United States port (or to any transaction or class of transactions at such port).

IMPLEMENTATION OF FINDINGS.—For purposes of section 4461(d)(2)(B) of the Internal Revenue Code of 1954, the findings of any study or review conducted pursuant to subsections (a) and (b) of this section shall be effective 60 days after notification to the ports concerned.

Thomas P. O'Neill

Speaker of the House of Representatives.

Strom Thurmond

Vice-President of the United States and
President of the Senate pro tempore.

APPROVED

NOV 17 1986

Ronald Reagan

Civil Works, Congress, and the Executive Branch

From the beginning, both Congress and the Secretary of the Army carefully monitored and guided the involvement of the Corps of Engineers in civil works projects. In fact, in 1800 it was Secretary of War James McHenry who suggested that engineer officers possess talents that serve the country not only in war but also in peacetime "works of a civil nature."

Once the Corps was permanently established in 1802, few operational and organizational changes were made without explicit authorization of the Secretary of War. Indeed, the Chief of the Engineer Department, along with the chiefs of other War Department bureaus, enjoyed direct access to the Secretary of War and protested vehemently whenever the Army Commanding General attempted to interfere with that access. Even the correspondence procedures reflected this close relationship. Mail intended for the Chief Engineer was sent under cover to the Secretary of War, with the words "Engineer Department" written on the lower left-hand corner of the envelope. Conversely, reports from the Army engineers intended for Congress were transmitted through the Secretary of War. The precise role of the Army Commanding General was not clarified until the position of Army Chief of Staff was created at the beginning of the 20th century.

Examples of early oversight activities of the secretaries of war are numerous. John C. Calhoun did not hesitate giving guidance to the Board for Internal Improvements, organized in 1824 to administer the responsibilities imposed by the General Survey Act. Charles M. Conrad transferred certain civil works responsibilities from the Topographical Engineers to the Corps of Engineers following passage of the

John C. Calhoun, Secretary of War (December 1817 to March 1825).

1852 Rivers and Harbors Act. His successor, Jefferson Davis, allowed the use of local funds to continue projects that had already received some congressional appropriations. In these and other ways, the secretaries of war profoundly influenced

Charles M. Conrad, Secretary of War (August 1850 to March 1853).

Extract from the Water Resources Development Act of 1986 (P.L. 99-662).

127

the organization and direction of the Army engineers.

Meanwhile, Congress also helped mold the operations and policies of the Corps of Engineers. It not only appropriated funds and authorized civil works projects, but it also specified how many officers the Corps was to have, conditions for their promotion, and even how much per diem (if any) they should earn while assigned to a project. Congress authorized oversight boards of engineer officers and determined what precise responsibilities the boards were to discharge. It requested surveys and reports, and congressional committees carefully reviewed the Corps' progress on its civil works assignments, rarely failing to call attention to a real or imagined defect in the Corps' management. The responsibility of the Engineer Department to carry out the wishes of Congress, including the development of "internal improvements," was explicitly noted in the General Regulations of the Army (1825).

After the Civil War, the congressional role in Corps affairs became even more evident. While not appreciably increasing the number of officers assigned to the Corps, Congress substantially increased the Corps' work on rivers and harbors. Consequently, the Corps was forced to depend on help from the civilian engineer community. This dependence worked to the Corps' disadvantage. Most of these engineers did not become career employees of the Corps, but the very fact of their employment helped give credibility to the charge that the Corps was unable to fulfill its civil works functions. Civil engineers maintained that they, not military engineers, should be in charge of civil works. They lobbied Congress, and their congressional sympathizers introduced numerous bills in the 1880s to transfer civil works functions from the Corps of Engineers to some other part of government; often, the preferred solution was to create a new Department of Public Works. Railroad interests,

Theodore E. Burton, representative (twelve terms) and senator (two terms) from Ohio.

Senate Historical Office

which perceived the Corps as an unfair competitor in the development of national transportation systems, wished to have the private sector do all rivers and harbors work. Pummeled from many quarters, the Corps saw its relationship with Congress become at once more dependent and more fractious.

Authorizations and appropriations during this period reflected some of the worst evils of pork-barrel legislation. Projects were poorly chosen, piecemeal appropriations were commonplace, and the Corps of Engineers often gave unreliable estimates. About the turn of the century, matters briefly took a turn for the better, mainly as a result of the work of Ohio Representative Theodore E. Burton. As chairman of the Rivers and Harbors Committee, he shepherded through Congress a bill establishing the Board of Engineers for Rivers and Harbors within the Corps of Engineers to examine costs, benefits, and necessity of rivers and harbors improvements. In the 1907 Rivers and Harbors Act, Burton did not allow one new project to be added unless the entire cost of the project was appropriated and it had the express approval of the Chief of Engineers. Had this practice of avoiding piecemeal appropriations and unjustified projects continued, some of the worst examples of traditional pork-barrel legislation never would have been approved. Instead, after Burton's departure from the House in 1909, Congress quickly reverted to its old ways. The 1910 Rivers and Harbors Act appropriated funds for projects in 226 of the 391 congressional districts.

While Congress busily gave the Corps work, the secretaries of war attempted to oversee the Corps' execution of its civil works projects. This attention to Corps operations may have been a matter of choice with some secretaries, but several rivers and harbors acts passed in the 1880s explicitly charged the Secretary of War to supervise the expenditure of appropriated funds in order, in the words of the 1884 act, to "secure a judicious and economical expenditure of said sums." The Secretary was directed furthermore to submit to Congress annual reports of work done, contracts made, and funds expended. Pursuant to these acts, the Secretary of War issued new regulations in 1887 that specifically delegated to the Chief of Engineers the responsibility to supervise "all disbursements by officers of the Corps." Slightly modified in 1889, these regulations also charged the Chief of Engineers to present to the Secretary of War an annual report of Engineer Department operations and, "with the approbation of the Secretary of War," to determine the quality, number, and physical characteristics of equipment needed by the Army engineers. The Secretary of War approved the assignment of division engineers as well as officers to serve on the board that oversaw fortifications and rivers and harbors improvements. He approved the initiation of new projects and specified the forms to be used to contract work. Moreover, he approved any modifications of the original contract. Finally, it should be noted that it was the Secretary of War, not the Chief of Engineers, whom Congress charged to have surveys done, civil works projects constructed, and rules issued to regulate federally operated canals and waterways. The work, of course, was then assigned to the Corps of Engineers.

In the Progressive Era at the beginning of the 20th century, the Secretary of War's office became embroiled in the controversy over the development of multipurpose water projects. Multipurpose planners sought to develop coordinated river basin programs that responded to a wide variety of needs, including navigation, flood control, irrigation, water supply, and hydropower. The Corps of Engineers generally opposed the concept, arguing that other purposes should always be subordinated to navigation in federal projects, that multipurpose dams would be difficult to operate, and that greater coordination was not needed; existing government agencies could provide whatever coordination was required. However, multipurpose development supporters had powerful friends in Congress, especially Senator Francis G. Newlands of Nevada, who introduced legislation to establish a multipurpose water resources coordinating commission. Henry L.

Henry L. Stimson, Secretary of War (May 1911 to March 1913 and July 1940 to September 1945) and Secretary of State (March 1929 to March 1933).

Stimson, President Taft's Secretary of War, was an avid conservationist and a former member of the board of directors of the National Conservation Association. He wholeheartedly supported the Newlands measure. So did Newton D. Baker, who served under President Wilson. Other secretaries, such as William H. Taft, who headed the War Department before he succeeded Theodore Roosevelt as President, and Lindley M. Garrison, who served in Wilson's first administration, were more sympathetic toward the Corps.

Secretary of War Stimson complained about his relationship with the Chief of Engineers. Stimson would ask the Chief whether an improvement should be made in light of other demands on the budget. Without answering the question, the Chief of Engineers, Brigadier General William H. Bixby, simply would maintain that the project would be good for the country, without comparing it with other projects or budgetary demands. Stimson pursued his point. He wanted to use a comparative approach. However, Bixby objected, "I have nothing to do with that. I cannot have anything to do with it. Congress will not listen to me on that. They reserve the judgment to do that themselves." Stimson thought the Corps was uncooperative and unresponsive, but there was some merit in the argument of the Chief of Engineers. As Newlands himself pointed out, numerous rivers and harbors acts had indeed constrained the Corps' flexibility. While the Corps had authority only to recommend a project based on its own merits, it did seem to support projects that were politically feasible and not necessarily urgently required. Also, the Corps' opposition to a more constructive, integrated, approach in water resources

Idealized view of sound water management integrating flood control, navigation, irrigation, water power, recreation, water supply, wastewater management, and soil conservation components.

A Water Policy for the American People, President's Water Resources Policy Commission, 1950

management reflected a predictable bureaucratic concern for maintaining maximum administrative independence.

The 1925 Rivers and Harbors Act accelerated the movement toward multipurpose water management. It authorized the Corps and the Federal Power Commission to prepare cost estimates for surveys of navigable streams and tributaries "whereon power development appears feasible and practicable." The aim was to develop plans to improve stream navigation "in combination with the most efficient development of the potential water power, the control of floods, and the needs of irrigation." The Corps responded with a recommendation for 24 surveys at an estimated cost of $7.3 million. In 1927 Congress appropriated the necessary funds, whereupon the Corps launched a series of comprehensive river surveys. The resulting reports became known as the "308 reports" after the House document in which the survey estimates had first appeared. They became basic planning documents for many of the multipurpose projects undertaken by the federal government just before and after World War II. In 1935 Congress authorized the Corps to supplement the 308 reports with studies "to take into account important changes in economic factors as they occur and additional streamflow records or other factual data." This authority charged the Corps with a broad responsibility to undertake continuing river basin planning, with the emphasis on navigation and flood control.

From about 1885 to 1925, the federal presence in the daily routine of private individuals became more and more visible. Working with the executive branch, Congress attempted to control abuses that could threaten the liberty, livelihood, or

health of the citizenry. To do so, it was necessary to increase the regulatory authority of various federal agencies, including the Department of War. In 1886 Congress gave the Secretary authority to regulate harbor lines. The 1890 Rivers and Harbors Act expanded the Secretary's authority to regulate and have removed any navigation obstructions, including bridges, waste material, and structures, such as dams and piers, built outside established harbor lines. In 1894 Congress authorized the War Department to regulate navigation in all federally owned canals, regardless of whether the Corps had built them or not. The 1899 Rivers and Harbors Act gave the Secretary added authority to regulate the dumping of waste material into navigable streams and the construction of any structures that might impede navigation. The 1906 General Dam Act authorized the Secretary of War to review and approve plans and specifications for all dams to be constructed across navigable waters. While, of course, most of these new responsibilities were delegated to the Corps of Engineers, in no case did Congress bypass the Secretary and grant power directly to the Chief of Engineers.

The Corps' relationship with Congress in the interwar period was extremely close. Indeed, Secretary of War George H. Dern called

the Corps "an agency of the legislative branch" in a 1934 report to the President. Congress did not just establish overall water resources policy, but congressional committees also determined which projects should be funded and the extent and timing of the funding. One procedure that was used extensively was the committee review resolution, which required the Corps to reconsider reports in which it had recommended against project construction. This was a particularly popular device during the New Deal, when projects were needed for work relief as well as for navigation or flood control. For instance, only about one-third of the projects authorized in the 1935 Rivers and Harbors Act originated as favorable reports. Reports on most of the others had been modified in response to a committee review resolution. The procedure constituted a kind of quasi-legislative process that circumvented both the rest of Congress and the executive branch.

Corps Orders and Regulations directed district engineers to contact each member of Congress within their districts in order to solicit the congressman's wishes about desired rivers and harbors improvements. The congressman was also invited to testify at a public hearing dealing with the project and to present written arguments to the Board of Engineers for Rivers and Harbors,

George H. Dern, Secretary of War
(March 1933 to 1936).

which reviewed the project report. If the congressman was still dissatisfied, then he always had recourse to the committee review resolution. While this kind of relationship could have led to tension, such was not the case. Congressmen protected the Corps at the same time they pressured it. All efforts by President Franklin D. Roosevelt to centralize water resources planning and institute some Progressive Era ideas met immovable congressional (and War Department) opposition; the Corps remained the water resources agency of choice in both wings of the Capitol.

When Congress passed the 1936 Flood Control Act, officially recognizing a federal obligation in flood control activity, it expanded enormously the responsibilities of the Corps of Engineers. The law authorized the expenditure of $320 million for about 250 projects and a number of examinations and surveys. Since 1936, the Corps has built, pursuant to congressional authorizations and appropriations, over 300 reservoirs whose primary benefit is flood control.

President Roosevelt attempted to ensure interagency coordination of federal water projects. In 1939 he instructed the Departments of War, Interior, and Agriculture to cooperate with his National Resources Planning Board in drawing up a memorandum that would ensure consultation among all federal water agencies during project planning. The subsequent tripartite agreement resulted in better and more information being exchanged among the agencies; however, it completely failed to eliminate bureaucratic rivalries. Roosevelt finally gave up on developing a centralized natural resources planning organization in 1943, when Congress refused to appropriate money to keep the National Resources Planning Board

in existence. However, the President continued to press one of the board's chief ideas, basin-wide planning commissions. His support of the Missouri Valley Authority reflected this commitment. A similar authority for the Columbia River basin was discussed, and Roosevelt's successor, Harry S. Truman, embraced the idea. Nevertheless, continued congressional skepticism assured that river basin commissions never would obtain the authority that Roosevelt and Truman envisioned.

Although the National Resources Planning Board was eliminated in 1943, federal agencies continued to coordinate their various responsibilities. The Departments of War, Agriculture, and Interior established the Federal Interagency River Basin Committee (FIARBC), commonly called "Firebrick." Later, the Departments of Labor and Commerce and the Federal Security Agency (which supervised the Public Health Service) joined. Various technical subcommittees attempted to coordinate water development in specific river basins, usually meeting limited success. In 1954 President Eisenhower replaced the commission with the new Interagency Committee on Water Resources (IACWR). "Icewater," as this agency became known, had minimal impact since its desire

President Franklin Delano Roosevelt.

to strengthen executive authority elicited little interest in Congress.

The various official committees and study commissions, like the first and second Hoover Commissions, that existed in the post-World War II period mirrored an emerging consensus that rational water resources development required uniform procedures and ongoing coordination. However, executive branch committees such as Firebrick did not have the clout to be effective interagency managers. The organization in the executive branch that did seem to have the necessary visibility and bureaucratic authority was the Bureau of the Budget. Upon the dissolution of the National Resources Planning Board in 1943, President Roosevelt issued Executive Order 9384, which directed all federal public works agencies to submit to the bureau annually their updated long-range programs. The major goal seemed to be to ensure that the Bureau of the Budget had the opportunity to see how well agency long-range plans fit into the overall administrative program. Although the budget bureau attempted to create a new division to handle the review of agency programs, Congress refused to appropriate funds to hire personnel. Therefore, the bureau was forced to review the programs with existing personnel. The result was a limited review that ignored such issues as the conformance of agency water project plans with regional plans, social utility, or reliability of the cost/benefit analysis.

However, the Bureau of the Budget drafted and sent to all federal water resources agencies in December 1952 a far-reaching directive pertaining to the planning of water projects. Simply known as Circular A-47, the document stipulated that the benefits of each purpose in a multipurpose project must exceed the costs; it would no longer

suffice for the total benefits to exceed total costs. It also directed that 50 years would be the maximum allowable time for the repayment of a federal investment. Although the guidance was criticized in Congress, it remained the basic planning document for the next decade and placed the Bureau of the Budget in the middle of the ongoing debate over water resources planning.

The Eisenhower administration attempted to place individual projects in the context of other national priorities and was generally skeptical of massive dam-building projects. The Bureau of the Budget generally looked far more favorably at smaller urban flood control projects. Moreover, budget personnel advocated reducing the planning period if at all possible in order to move ahead with actual construction. Of course, Congress could and often did insert projects into bills that not only had not received bureau approval, but had not even been recommended by the Corps of Engineers. For instance, a 1956 bill vetoed by Eisenhower would have authorized 32 projects that had not been reviewed by the Corps. A 1958 bill, also vetoed, would have authorized four projects, costing $27 million, that had no project reports and another three projects, costing $115 million, that had a negative cost/benefit ratio. In 1959 Congress passed a bill over a presidential veto. Eisenhower had disapproved the bill because of the expense involved, some $800 million.

The history of federal water resources development in the third quarter of the 20th century has two general themes: the growing influence of the Bureau of the Budget over water policy on the one hand and, on the other, the continuation of pork-barrel politics to determine actual project authorizations. Despite the budget bureau's occasionally successful efforts to convince the President to veto a "budget-busting" bill, in general Congress got its way. The bureau could delay projects by not including them in the budget submissions to Congress or by impounding funds for congressional new starts. However, the funds would often be made available in short order, and Congress would insert the projects it desired when it rewrote the administration budget. Congress attempted to conceal the final cost of projects by voting appropriations on a year-to-year basis. Rarely were projects fully funded at the beginning. Most congressmen realized that, had full funding been attempted, large water resources projects would have become politically unpalatable.

The Bureau of the Budget's growing involvement in water resources policy, coupled with a num-

Eugene W. Weber, Deputy Director of Civil Works for Policy, Office of the Chief of Engineers. Weber chaired the board that reviewed the entire civil works program and was an influential civil works policy maker in the post-World War II period.

ber of highly publicized attacks on the Corps' civil works program in the decade after World War II, weakened the Corps' ability to influence policy, even though it continued to administer the largest water resources program. Complicating the problem was a lack of leadership in this area at the secretarial level. In the immediate post-World War II period, first the Department of War and then (after July 1947) the Department of Army considered civil works as somewhat of a wayward waif within the country's military structure. In fact, the secretaries of the Army were quite content to leave such matters as dams, floodwalls, and levees to the Corps and its friends on Capitol Hill. Within the Army's senior bureaucracy, civil functions were bounced from office to office.

In 1950 Secretary of the Army Gordon Gray placed civil works under the newly created Assistant Secretary of the Army, General Management. When the holder of that position, Karl Bendetsen, became the Under Secretary of the Army in May 1952, the civil works responsibility moved with him. Some two years later, Congress raised the number of assistant secretaries in the military departments from two to four, and civil works was attached to the new Office of the Assistant Secretary of the Army, Civil-Military Affairs. However, that office was eliminated in 1958, and civil works was attached to the Office of the Assistant Secretary of the Army, Manpower and Reserve Affairs. This change reflected the clout of Dewey Short, who had moved from Secretary for Civil-Military Affairs to Secretary for Manpower and Reserve, rather than any sound administrative policy.

The waif continued to be shuttled around the hallways of the Pentagon in succeeding years. During the Kennedy administration, it found a home in the General Counsel's office, and the General Counsel obtained a second title, Special Assistant to the Secretary for Civil Functions. For a while, too, the title of Special Assistant to the Secretary for Civil Functions passed to the Deputy Under Secretary of the Army for International Affairs, Harry McPherson. McPherson observed that overseeing the Corps of Engineers "was an exercise in amiable futility." Although, like other military organizations in the United States, McPherson continued, the Corps was under civilian control, "in its case the controlling civilians were on the Hill" rather than in the Pentagon. Nevertheless, when Alfred B. Fitt became the General Counsel in 1964, he decided to be the Special Assistant in fact as well as in name.

At about the same time that Fitt became General Counsel, Secretary of the Army Cyrus Vance established a small, three-man board to review the entire civil works program. One of the board's major findings was that the Secretary of the Army should "participate personally and through his Secretariat" in water resources matters that involved participation by secretaries in other agencies of the executive branch. Board members specifically called for the creation of an assistant secretary of the Army "with responsibilities primarily for the civil works mission." Clearly, the board believed that interagency coordination and the growth of the civil works budget relative to the national budget required secretarial-level overview. Since the Secretary of the Army needed to give priority to more traditional military responsibilities, the obvious solution was to create an additional assistant secretary position. Of course, this required legislative authorization, but it appears that the board was reasonably confident such authorization could be obtained. They suggested in their report that "sources outside the Army" had advocated the creation of a new Assistant Secretary for Civil Works position, and it seems likely that at least some of

these sources were representatives and senators.

Another factor that contributed to the momentum to establish the position of Assistant Secretary for Civil Works was the 1965 decision of the President Lyndon B. Johnson to initiate the Planning, Programming, Budgeting (PPB) System throughout the federal agencies. First advanced by Secretary of Defense Robert McNamara in the Pentagon, the program was designed to allow for closer oversight of executive programs. While few federal agencies reacted enthusiastically to the presidential order, one that did was the Army's Office of Civil Functions. In 1965 Fitt established a Systems Analysis Group to develop new procedures for preparing the civil works budget and to draft a long-range water investment program for the nation. Group members proposed to shift emphasis from individual projects—the details of which were familiar only to the members of Congress directly concerned—to water resources problems in the various regions of the nation. Under Robert E. Jordan III, Army General Counsel and Special Assistant to the Secretary of the Army for Civil Functions, the Systems Analysis Group perfected a budgeting system and a five-year investment program based on regional allocations. This new approach was firmly installed in the Corps. Ultimately, however, neither the Bureau of the Budget nor Congress proved capable of shedding the project-by-project orientation in favor of a more programmatic approach to civil works budgeting. Still, the creation by Fitt and the use by Jordan of the Systems Analysis Group initiated an oversight and broadening of the Corps' civil works program that was far removed from the benign neglect of the preceding decade, and it presaged the establishment of the position of Assistant Secretary for Civil Works.

Utah Senator Frank E. Moss' attempt to establish a Department of Natural Resources, which would have included the Corps' civil works functions, and the nearly successful attempt in 1968 to put a congres-

sional moratorium on public works projects signified the gradual dissolution of the Corps' traditionally strong water resources constituency in Congress. Under Jordan and with the powerful support of Jordan's capable successor, Under Secretary of the Army Thaddeus Beal, the Systems Analysis Group pressed for new Corps missions: wastewater management and urban studies. While these initiatives failed to produce new construction responsibilities for the Corps, the experience showed that a secretarial-level political appointee who focused on civil works would be of enormous benefit. He could help strengthen planning and review functions within the Corps and, concurrently, give the Corps more clout within the executive branch, such as in the interdepartmental Water Resources Council, established in 1965.

Finally, mainly through the efforts of California Representative Don Clausen, a section was inserted in the 1970 Flood Control Act that authorized the position of Assistant Secretary of the Army, Civil Works. However, it was to be another five years before the first Assistant Secretary was appointed. This was largely because President Richard Nixon supported the creation of a new Department of Environment and Natural Resources

Victor V. Veysey, Assistant Secretary of the Army for Civil Works (March 1975 to January 1977).

and did not wish to do anything that appeared to strengthen the Corps' civil works mission. Finally, on March 20, 1975, Victor V. Veysey, a former Representative from California, was sworn in as the first Assistant Secretary of the Army for Civil Works. He served until January 1977.

As the first Assistant Secretary of the Army for Civil Works, Veysey had the difficult task of defining both his mission and his relationship with the Corps of Engineers. His approach was to act the "honest broker" between the Corps and other organizations involved with water resources; it was an approach that succeeding secretaries emulated. While working to be a conduit between the Corps and its environmental opponents, Veysey never lost the high respect he had for the Corps. He acted forcefully on certain issues, but he looked upon his role primarily as an advisory one. "I wasn't about to order the Chief of Engineers to do anything because I couldn't; that wasn't my role. He takes his orders from the Army Chief of Staff. But influence, yes. We could try to influence him in directions and in policy, procedure, and so forth. . . . But from the post of Assistant Secretary you don't order the Chief of Engineers to do anything."

President Jimmy Carter, who questioned the necessity of many water projects and emphasized environmental concerns, did not appoint an Assistant Secretary until April 1978. He chose Michael Blumenfeld, who also served as Deputy Under Secretary of the Army. Blumenfeld was not confirmed as Assistant Secretary until April 1979. Working through the Water Resources Council, he exerted strong leadership to develop new, environmentally sensitive principles and standards to guide the planning of water projects.

With the transfer of power from a Democratic to a Republican administration in 1981 came new water resources priorities. The new Assistant Secretary for Civil Works, William R. Gianelli, had formerly headed California's Department of Water Resources under then Gover-

nor Ronald Reagan. His objectives were to reform the regulatory program and to develop new ways to fund the Corps' water resources projects.

Both objectives reflected political and philosophical shifts. Gianelli considered the Corps' responsibility to regulate the dredging and filling of wetlands a water quality issue and not a mandate to protect wetlands. He changed regulatory procedures to shorten the processing time, partly by limiting the traditional way of appealing permit decisions. He also led early Reagan administration efforts to reduce the federal financial burden in activities that he believed nonfederal interests could and should fund.

Michael Blumenfeld, Assistant Secretary of the Army for Civil Works (April 1979 to January 1981).

William R. Gianelli, Assistant Secretary of the Army for Civil Works (April 1981 to May 1984).

Robert K. Dawson, Assistant Secretary of the Army for Civil Works (December 1985 to May 1987).

Gianelli's work, together with an unexpected positive response by project sponsors, helped convince Congress that some sort of cost-sharing was necessary if sound water projects were to proceed. It fell to Gianelli's successor, Robert K. Dawson (appointed Acting Assis-tant Secretary in May 1985), work-ing with Congress, to bring the process to a successful conclusion. The Water Resources Development Act of 1986, signed into law on No-vember 17, 1986, signaled a major historical change in the financing of water projects. Cost-sharing became part of nearly every water project venture. At the same time, the act authorized about 300 new water projects and numerous stud-ies at an estimated cost of over $15 billion.

Under Dawson's successor, Robert W. Page, the Corps ad-

The White House

President Ronald Reagan signing the Water Resources Development Act of 1986. Members of the 99th Congress present (from the left) are Senators Pete V. Domenici (Water Resources Subcommittee, Environ-ment and Public Works Committee), Lloyd Bentsen (Ranking Minority Member, Environment and Public Works Committee), James Abdnor (Chairman, Water Resources Subcommittee, Environment and Public Works Committee), Daniel Patrick Moynihan (Ranking Minority Member, Water Resources Subcommittee, Environment and Public Works Com-mittee), and Robert T. Stafford (Chairman, Environment and Public Works Committee), Representative Robert A. Roe (Chairman, Water Resources Subcommittee, House Committee on Public Works and Transportation), John O. Marsh, Jr. (Secretary of the Army), Repre-sentative James J. Howard (Chairman, House Committee on Public Works and Transportation), Robert K. Dawson (Assistant Secretary of the Army for Civil Works), Representative Mario Biaggi (Vice Chairman, House Committee on Merchant Marine and Fisheries), Representative Helen Delich Bentley (Water Resources Subcommittee, House Public Works and Transportation Committee), and Representative Arlan Stan-geland (Ranking Minority Member, Water Resources Subcommittee, House Public Works and Transportation Committee).

dressed a wide range of subjects to make project development—from planning through construction—more efficient, faster, and cheaper without sacrificing quality. The Corps rewrote planning procedures to ensure that nonfederal project sponsors, principally states and local communities, were full partners in project development.

After Page left office in October 1990, his position was not filled until July 1991, when Nancy Dorn became the first female Assistant Secretary of the Army for Civil Works. Perhaps more than her predecessors, Dorn was conservative about seeking new missions. She emphasized instead effective management of the Corps' existing missions.

Under secretaries Dorn and Page, the Corps undertook major reforms of the wetlands regulatory program. Policy guidance and changes in interagency agreements gave the Corps more authority in regulating the dredge and fill program assigned to the agency in the 1972 Clean Water Act. Strict time frames and guidelines were adopted governing other agencies' input to permit actions. Progress was made to ensure that agencies used the same definitions and standards to determine wetland jurisdictions.

With the change in administrations in January 1993, Dorn left office. After a prolonged period in which acting assistant secretaries served, H. Martin Lancaster became the first Assistant Secretary for Civil Works in the Clinton administration. Lancaster sought to reduce the time and cost of Corps studies and expand engineering and construction management opportunities for the Corps through its reimbursable Support for Others Program. The new Assistant

Secretary, a former member of Congress from North Carolina, improved communications with Congress and provided consistent support for the administration's environmental initiatives, especially the restoration of the Everglades and South Florida ecosystem.

Acting through the Assistant Secretary's office, the Secretary of the Army has assumed leadership of the Corps' civil works program. Although form and style vary according to administration, the Assistant Secretary helps ensure that the Corps remains the flexible, competent engineering organization that has continuously served the country for two centuries in peace and war.

Robert W. Page, Assistant Secretary of the Army for Civil Works (December 1987 to October 1990).

Nancy P. Dorn, Assistant Secretary of the Army for Civil Works (July 1991 to January 1993).

H. Martin Lancaster, Assistant Secretary of the Army for Civil Works (January 1996 to June 1997).

The Corps Castle

The appropriateness of the turreted castle as a symbol of the Corps of Engineers is readily apparent. The medieval castle is inseparably connected with fortification and architecture. In heraldry, the castle and the tower are often used in a coat of arms or given as charges in the shield of persons who reduced them, were the first to mount their walls in an assault, or successfully defended them. In this country the term "castle" has been applied to the strongest of our early fortifications, such as Castle Pinckney in Charleston, South Carolina, and Castles Williams and Clinton in New York Harbor, which, together with the entire system of permanent defense of our country, are particular achievements of the Corps of Engineers.

Possibly patterned after one of the city gates of Verdun, France, the castle is a highly conventionalized form, without decoration or embellishment. The Army officially announced the adoption of the castle, to appear on the Corps of Engineers' uniform epaulettes and belt plate, in 1840. Soon afterwards, the cadets at West Point, all of whom were part of the Corps of Engineers until the Military Academy came under the control of the Army-at-large in 1866, also wore the castle. Army regulations first prescribed the use of the castle on the cap in 1841. Subsequently, the castle appeared on the shoulder knot; on saddle cloth as a collar ornament; and on the buttons. Although its design has changed many times, the castle, since its inception, has remained the distinctive symbol of the Corps of Engineers.

US Army Corps of Engineers ®

Modern castle adopted after the Corps of Engineers became a Major Army Command (MACOM).

Both the modern castle and the traditional castle became Registered Trademarks of the U.S. Army Corps of Engineers in November 1993.

Traditional castle.

The Essayons Button

The Corps of Engineers' oldest and most time-honored insignia is the exclusive Essayons Button. It has not changed in basic design since its first definitely known use during the War of 1812. It is still the required button for the Army Engineers' uniform.

Evidence which could establish the actual facts concerning the designing and adoption of the Essayons Button probably burned at West Point in 1838, when the building containing the library and earliest official Corps and Military Academy records caught fire.

However, while early Army regulations mentioned the "button of the Engineers... with only the device and motto heretofore established,"

apparently no authoritative detailed description of the button appeared until 1840. The Army prescribed new uniforms on February 18, 1840, in General Orders 7, AGO, which officially described the button as follows:

"An eagle holding in his beak a scroll with the word, 'Essayons,' a bastion with embrasures in the distance, surrounded by water, and rising sun; the figures to be of dead gold upon a bright field."

In 1902, when the Army adopted "regulation" buttons, it allowed only the Corps of Engineers to retain its own distinctive Essayons Button in recognition of the distinguished traditions that it symbolized.

Portraits and Profiles

Since 1775, 49 officers have held the highest office among the Army's Engineers. In addition, three officers headed the Topographical Bureau and the Corps of Topographical Engineers between 1818 and 1863. Their likenesses and biographies are on the following pages. Ranks listed are the highest ranks, excluding brevet rank, attained while in office.

Colonel Richard Gridley
America's First Chief Engineer
(June 1775–April 1776)

Born January 3, 1710, in Boston, Massachusetts, Richard Gridley was the outstanding American military engineer during the French and Indian wars from the Siege of Louisburg in 1745 to the fall of Quebec. For his services he was awarded a commission in the British Army, a grant of the Magdalen Islands, 3,000 acres of land in New Hampshire, and a life annuity. When the break with the mother country came, he stood with the colonies and was made Chief Engineer in the New England Provincial Army. He laid out the defenses on Breed's Hill and was wounded at the Battle of Bunker Hill. He was appointed Chief Engineer of the Continental Army after Washington took command in July 1775. He directed the construction of the fortifications which forced the British to evacuate Boston in March 1776. When Washington moved his Army south, Gridley remained as Chief Engineer of the New England Department. He retired in 1781 at age 70. He died June 21, 1796, in Stoughton, Massachusetts.

Colonel Rufus Putnam
Chief Engineer, Continental Army
(April 1776–December 1776)

Rufus Putnam was born April 9, 1738, in Sutton, Massachusetts. A millwright by trade, his three years of Army service during the French and Indian War influenced him to study surveying and the art of war. After the Battle of Lexington, he was commissioned an officer of the line, but General Washington soon discovered his engineering abilities. He planned the fortifications on Dorchester Neck that convinced the British to abandon Boston. Washington then brought Putnam to New York as his Chief Engineer. He returned to infantry service in 1777, taking command of the

5th Massachusetts Regiment. He and his troops helped to fortify West Point, erecting strong defenses atop the steep hill that commanded that garrison. The remains of Fort Putnam, preserved by the Military Academy, still honor his

name there. Putnam was named a brigadier general in the Continental Army in 1783. In 1788 he led the first settlers to found the present town of Marietta, Ohio. The fortifications that he built there saved the settlements from annihilation during the disastrous Indian wars. He became Surveyor General of federal public lands and judge of the Supreme Court of Ohio. He died in Marietta on May 1, 1824.

Major General Louis Lebègue Duportail
Chief Engineer, Continental Army
(July 22, 1777–October 10, 1783)

One of General Washington's most trusted military advisors, Louis Lebègue Duportail was born near Orleans, France, in

1743. He graduated from the royal engineer school in Mézières, France, as a qualified

139

engineer officer in 1765. Promoted to lieutenant colonel in the Royal Corps of Engineers, Duportail was secretly sent to America in March 1777 to serve in Washington's Army under an agreement between Benjamin Franklin and the government of King Louis XVI of France. He was appointed colonel and commander of all engineers in the Continental Army, July 1777; brigadier general, November 1777; commander, Corps of Engineers, May 1779; and major general (for meritorious service), November 1781. Duportail participated in fortifications planning from Boston to Charleston and helped Washington evolve the primarily defensive military strategy that wore down the British Army. He also directed the construction of siege works at Yorktown, site of the decisive American victory of the war. Returning to France in October 1783, Duportail became an infantry officer and in 1788 a field marshal. He served as France's minister of war during the revolutionary years 1790 and 1791 and promoted military reforms. Forced into hiding by radical Jacobins, he escaped to America and bought a farm near Valley Forge, Pennsylvania. He lived there until 1802, when he died at sea while attempting to return to France.

Lieutenant Colonel Stephen Rochefontaine
Commandant, Corps of Artillerists and Engineers (February 26, 1795–May 7, 1798)

Born near Reims, France, in 1755, Stephen Rochefontaine came to America in 1778 after failing to gain a position in the French Royal Corps of En-

gineers. He volunteered in General Washington's Army on May 15, 1778, and was appointed captain in the Corps of Engineers on September 18, 1778. For his distinguished services at the siege of Yorktown, Rochefontaine was given the brevet rank of major by Congress, November 16, 1781. He returned to France in 1783 and served as an infantry officer, reaching the rank of colonel in the French Army. He came back to the United States in 1792. President Washington appointed him a civilian engineer to fortify the New England coast in 1794. After the new Corps of Artillerists and Engineers was organized, Washington made Rochefontaine a lieutenant colonel and commandant of the new Corps on February 26, 1795. Rochefontaine started a military school at West Point in 1795, but the building and all his equipment were burned the following year. He left the Army on May 7, 1798, and lived in New York City, where he died January 30, 1814. He is buried in old St. Paul's Cemetery in New York.

Lieutenant Colonel Henry Burbeck
Commandant, 1st Regiment of Artillerists and Engineers (May 7, 1798–April 1, 1802)

Born June 8, 1754, in Boston, Massachusetts, Henry Burbeck served as lieutenant of artillery under Colonel Richard Gridley, the Army's first Chief Engineer and artillery commander, in 1775. He remained in the Artillery Corps under General Henry Knox and in 1777 assumed command of a company of the 3d Continental Artillery Regiment. His unit remained in the North to defend the Hudson Highlands and marched into New York when the British evacuated that city at the close of the war. Honorably discharged in January 1784, Burbeck was reappointed captain of artillery in 1786 and

commanded the post at West Point, New York, in 1787–89.

He commanded the Army's Battalion of Artillery and served as General Anthony Wayne's Chief of Artillery in the Northwest in 1792–94. He commanded at Fort Mackinac in 1796–99. From 1798 to 1802 Burbeck was the senior regimental commander of artillerists and engineers. He also commanded the Eastern Department of the Army in 1800 and in that year endorsed the creation of a corps of engineers separate from the artillerists. He was Chief of the new Artillery Corps from 1802 to 1815, first as a colonel and then during the War of 1812 as a brevet brigadier general. During the Jefferson administration, Burbeck successfully developed and tested domestically produced cast-iron artillery pieces. He left the Army in June 1815 and died on October 2, 1848, in New London, Connecticut.

Colonel Jonathan Williams
Chief Engineer (and First Superintendent of West Point) (April 1, 1802–June 20, 1803, and April 19, 1805–July 31, 1812)

Jonathan Williams was born May 20, 1750, in Boston, Massachusetts, a grand-nephew of Benjamin Franklin. Williams spent most of the period from 1770 to 1785 in England and France, where

he assisted Franklin with business affairs and served as a commercial agent in Nantes. He joined the American Philosophical Society in 1788 and published articles on scientific subjects. President Adams appointed Williams a

major in the Corps of Artillerists and Engineers in February 1801, and President Jefferson made him the Army's Inspector of Fortifications and assigned him to lead the new Military Academy at West Point in December 1801. The following year Jefferson appointed him to command the separate Corps of Engineers established by Congress on March 16, 1802. From 1807 to 1812 Williams designed and completed construction of Castle Williams in New York Harbor, the first casemated battery in the United States. He founded the U.S. Military Philosophical Society and gave it its motto, "Science in War is the Guarantee of Peace." He resigned from the Army in 1812 and was heading a group of volunteer engineers building fortifications around Philadelphia when he was elected to Congress from that city in 1814. He died in Philadelphia on May 16, 1815.

Colonel Joseph Gardner Swift
Chief Engineer (July 31, 1812–November 12, 1818)

Born December 31, 1783, in Nantucket, Massachusetts, Joseph Swift was appointed a cadet by President John Adams and in 1802 became one of the first two graduates of the Military Academy. He constructed Atlantic coast fortifications, 1804–12, and was only 28 years old when appointed Colonel, Chief Engineer, and Superintendent of

the Military Academy in 1812. As Chief Engineer of the Northern Army, he distinguished himself at the Battle of Chrysler's Farm on November 11, 1813. After completing defensive works in New York, Swift was voted "Benefactor to the City" by the corporation in 1814. He helped to rebuild the burned capital in Washington. He also reorganized the academic staff and planned new buildings at the Military Academy. He resigned from the Army on November 12, 1818, and was appointed Surveyor of the Port of New York. He held that customs post until 1827. Swift was also one of the founders of the first New York Philharmonic Society in 1823. As Chief Engineer for various railroads, he laid the first "T" rail. From 1829 to 1845 Swift worked for the Corps of Engineers as a civilian, improving two harbors on Lake Ontario. He died July 23, 1865, in Geneva, New York.

Colonel Walker Keith Armistead
Chief Engineer
(November 12, 1818–June 1, 1821)

Born in Virginia in 1785, Walker Armistead was named a cadet in the Corps of Artillerists and Engineers by President Jefferson in 1801. On March 5, 1803, he became the third graduate of the new Military Academy and was commissioned in the Corps of Engineers. He served as superintending engineer of the

defenses of New Orleans and Norfolk. During the War of 1812, he was successively Chief Engineer of the Niagara frontier army and the forces defending Chesapeake Bay. He was promoted to colonel and Chief Engineer on November 12, 1818. When the Army was reorganized on June 1, 1821, he became commander of the 3d Artillery. He was brevetted brigadier

general in 1828. He commanded the United States troops that opposed the Seminole Indians in Florida in 1840–41. He died in Upperville, Virginia, October 13, 1845.

Colonel Alexander Macomb
Chief Engineer
(June 1, 1821–May 24, 1828)

Born April 3, 1782, in Detroit, Alexander Macomb entered the Army as a cornet of light dragoons in 1799 but was discharged in 1800. He returned

to the Army in 1801 as a second lieutenant of infantry and served as secretary of the commission negotiating treaties with the Indians of the Mississippi Territory. He joined the

Corps of Engineers in October 1802 as a first lieutenant and superintended construction of a depot, armory, and fortifications in the Carolinas and Georgia. He also wrote a treatise on military law. After rising to lieutenant colonel in the Corps of Engineers in 1810, he was appointed colonel, 3d Artillery, in 1812 and brigadier general in 1814. In the latter year he commanded the Lake Champlain frontier force that repulsed a larger veteran British army at Plattsburg. He was voted thanks and a gold medal by the Congress and brevetted major general. In the reorganized Army, he was appointed colonel and Chief Engineer, 1821. In that position, he administered the start of federal river and harbor improvements. He was elevated to Commanding General of the Army with the rank of major general in 1828. He died June 25, 1841, in Washington, D.C., and was buried with the highest military honors in Congressional Cemetery. Macomb made the earliest known drawing (1807) to resemble the engineer button.

Colonel Charles Gratiot
Chief Engineer
(May 24, 1828–December 6, 1838)

Charles Gratiot was born August 29, 1786, in St. Louis. President Jefferson appointed him cadet in 1804. He graduated from the Military Academy in 1806 and was commissioned in the Corps of Engineers. He became a captain in 1808 and assisted Macomb in constructing fortifications in Charleston, South Carolina. He was post commander of West Point in 1810–11. He distinguished himself as General William Henry Harrison's Chief Engineer in the War of 1812. He served as Chief Engineer in Michigan Territory (1817–18), and superintending engineer, construction of Hampton Roads defenses (1819–28). On May 24, 1828, Gratiot was appointed colonel of engineers, brevet

brigadier general, and Chief Engineer. For ten years he administered an expanding program of river, harbor, road,

and fortification construction. He also engaged in a lengthy dispute with War Department officials over benefits, and in 1838 President Van Buren dismissed him for failing to repay government funds in his custody. Gratiot became a clerk in the General Land Office and died May 18, 1855, in St. Louis.

Brigadier General Joseph Gilbert Totten
Chief Engineer
(December 7, 1838–April 22, 1864)

Born August 23, 1788, in New Haven, Connecticut, Joseph Totten graduated from the Military Academy and was

commissioned in the Corps of Engineers on July 1, 1805. He resigned in 1806 to assist his uncle, Major Jared Mansfield, who was then serving as Surveyor General of federal public lands. Totten re-entered the Corps of Engineers in 1808 and assisted in building Castle Williams and other New York Harbor defenses. During the War of 1812, he was Chief Engineer of the Niagara frontier and Lake Champlain armies. He was brevetted lieutenant colonel for gallant conduct in the Battle of Plattsburg. As a member of the first permanent Board of Engineers, 1816, he laid down durable principles of coast defense construction. Appointed Chief Engineer in 1838, he served in that position for 25 years. He was greatly admired by General Winfield Scott, for whom he directed the siege of Veracruz as his Chief Engineer during the Mexican War. He was regent of the Smithsonian Institution and cofounder of the National Academy of Sciences. He died April 22, 1864, in Washington, D.C.

Major Isaac Roberdeau
Chief, Topographical Bureau (August 1, 1818–January 15, 1829)

Isaac Roberdeau was born in Philadelphia, Pennsylvania, on September 11, 1763. He studied engineering in London, returning to America in 1787 to write, survey, and pursue astronomy. In 1791–92 he assisted Pierre L'Enfant in planning the new federal capital, the future Washington, D.C. For the next two decades, he practiced engineering in Pennsylvania. His work

included assisting William Weston on a canal connecting the Schuykill and Susque-

hanna rivers. During the War of 1812, he served in the Army as a major of topographical engineers, employed chiefly on fortifications. After the war he assisted the Canadian boundary survey. Secretary of War Calhoun appointed Roberdeau in 1818 to head the newly created Topographical Bureau of the War Department. At first his duties were largely custodial; he prepared returns and maintained books, maps, and scientific equipment. As the nation turned its attention to internal improvement, Roberdeau used his position to promote the civil activities of the topographical engineers. He was brevetted lieutenant colonel in 1823. He died in Georgetown, D.C., on January 15, 1829.

Colonel John James Abert
Chief, Topographical Bureau (January 31, 1829–April 11, 1861)
Chief, Corps of Topographical Engineers (July 7, 1838–September 9, 1861)

Born September 17, 1788, in Frederick, Maryland, John Abert received an appointment as a Military Academy cadet in January 1808. In 1811 he took a position in the War Department in Washington and resigned as cadet. He joined the District of Columbia Militia as a private during the War of 1812 and fought at the Battle of Bladensburg. In November 1814 he was appointed a topographical engineer with the brevet rank of major. He worked on fortifications, surveys, and river and harbor improvements before being appointed Chief, Topographical Bureau, in 1829. Abert headed the Corps of Topographical Engineers from its creation by

Congress in 1838 until he retired in 1861. Under his leadership the Corps of Topographical Engineers improved

the navigability of rivers and harbors, particularly in the basins of the Mississippi River and the Great Lakes; conducted a survey of the hydraulics of the lower Mississippi River; constructed lighthouses and marine hospitals; explored large portions of the West; and conducted military, border, and railroad surveys. Colonel Abert died in Washington, D.C., on January 27, 1863.

Colonel Stephen H. Long
Chief, Topographical Bureau (September 9, 1861–March 3, 1863)
Chief, Corps of Topographical Engineers (December 12, 1861–March 3, 1863)

Born in Hopkinton, New Hampshire, December 30, 1784, Stephen Long graduated from Dartmouth in 1809 and was commissioned in the

Corps of Engineers in 1814. Brevetted major, Topographical Engineers, in April 1816, he conducted extensive explorations and surveys in the old

Northwest and Great Plains. Long's Peak was named in his honor. He fixed the nation's northern boundary at the 49th parallel at Pembina, North Dakota, in 1823. He conducted surveys in the Appalachians for the Baltimore and Ohio Railroad and in 1829 published his *Railroad Manual or a Brief Exposition of Principles and Deductions Applicable in Tracing the Route of a Railroad.* He served for years as Chief Engineer for improvement of the western rivers, with headquarters in Cincinnati, Louisville, and finally St. Louis. He became Chief, Corps of Topographical Engineers, in 1861. Upon consolidation of the two corps on March 3, 1863, Colonel Long became senior officer to the Chief Engineer, Corps of Engineers. He retired that year and died in Alton, Illinois, September 4, 1864.

Brigadier General Richard Delafield
Chief Engineer (April 22, 1864–August 8, 1866)

Born September 1, 1798, in New York City, Richard Delafield was the first graduate of the Military Academy to receive a merit class standing, ranking first in the class of 1818. Commissioned in the Corps of Engineers, he was a topographical engineer with the American commission to establish the northern boundary under the Treaty of Ghent. He served as assistant engineer in the construction of Hampton Roads defenses (1819–24) and was in charge of fortifications and surveys in the Mississippi River Delta area (1824–32). While superintendent of repair work on the Cumberland Road east of

142 The Historical Society of Pennsylvania

the Ohio River, he designed and built the first cast-iron tubular-arch bridge in the United States. Appointed Superintendent of the Military Academy after the fire in 1838, he designed the new buildings and the new cadet uniform that first displayed the castle insignia. He superintended the construction of coast defenses for New York Harbor (1846–55), was a military observer at the siege of Sevastopol, and was again Superintendent of the Military Academy (1856–61). He was in charge of New York Harbor defenses (1861–64) and Chief Engineer from 1864 until his retirement in 1866. He died November 5, 1873, in Washington, D.C. The Secretary of War ordered that 13 guns be fired in his memory at West Point.

Brigadier General Andrew Atkinson Humphreys
Chief of Engineers (August 8, 1866–June 30, 1879)

Andrew Humphreys was born November 2, 1810, in Philadelphia, the son and grandson of chiefs of naval construction. His grandfather designed *Old Ironsides.* Young Humphreys graduated from the Military Academy in 1831 and served as an artillery officer in Florida during the Seminole War. He resigned from the Army in 1836 but accepted an appointment as first lieutenant in the new Corps of Topographical Engineers in 1838. He led a survey of the Mississippi River Delta and in

1854–61 headed the Office of Pacific Railroad Explorations and Surveys. His co-written *Report Upon the Physics and Hydraulics of the Mississippi River*, translated into several languages, became a classic in hydraulic literature. General Humphreys, a distinguished Civil War army corps commander, became Chief of Engineers in 1866. He established the Engineer School of Application and oversaw a substantial expansion of the Corps' river and harbor work.

Humphreys held a Harvard degree, published Civil War histories, and was cofounder of the National Academy of Sciences. He died December 27, 1883, in Washington, D.C.

Brigadier General Horatio Gouverneur Wright
Chief of Engineers (June 30, 1879–March 6, 1884)

Born March 6, 1820, in Clinton, Connecticut, Horatio Wright graduated second in the Military Academy class of 1841 and was commissioned in the Corps of Engineers. He superintended construction at Fort Jefferson at Dry Tortugas, 70 miles west of Key West, Florida, 1846–56. While assistant to the Chief Engineer of the Army, 1856–61, he was a member of boards to study iron carriages for seacoast guns and the adaptability of the 15-inch gun for ordnance. He co-wrote a "Report on Fabrication of Iron for Defenses." From Chief Engineer of a division at the first Battle of Bull Run, he advanced to command the famous 6th Army Corps, which saved Washing-

ton, D.C., from capture in 1864 and spearheaded the final assault on Petersburg and the pursuit of Lee to Appomattox in 1865. He commanded the Department of Texas, 1865–66, and served as a member of the Board of Engineers for Fortifications and many river and harbor planning boards until he was appointed Chief of Engineers in 1879. While Wright was

Chief of Engineers, engineer officers began a reservoir system at the headwaters of the Mississippi River and initiated the first substantial federal effort to control the river's lower reaches. General Wright retired March 6, 1884, and died July 2, 1899, in Washington, D.C.

Brigadier General John Newton
Chief of Engineers (March 6, 1884–August 27, 1886)

Born August 24, 1823, in Norfolk, Virginia, a city his father represented in Congress for 31 years, John Newton ranked second in the Military Academy class of 1842 and was commissioned in the Corps of Engineers. He taught engineering at the Military Academy (1843–46) and constructed fortifications along the Atlantic coast and Great Lakes (1846–52). He was a member of a special Gulf coast defense board (1856)

and Chief Engineer, Utah Expedition (1858). Though a fellow Virginian, he did not follow Robert E. Lee but stood firm for the Union. Newton helped construct Washington defenses and led a brigade at Antietam. As division commander, he stormed Marye's Heights at Fredericksburg and fought at Gettysburg and the siege of Atlanta. He commanded the Florida districts in 1864–66. Returning to the Corps, he oversaw improvements to the waterways around New York City and to the Hudson River above Albany. He also had charge of New York Harbor defenses until he was appointed Chief of Engineers in 1884. He is famed for blowing up New York's Hell Gate Rock with 140 tons of dynamite detonated on October 10, 1885. He retired from the Army in

1886 and served as Commissioner of Public Works, New York City (1886–88), and as President of the Panama Railroad Company (1888–95). He died May 1, 1895, in New York.

Brigadier General James Chatham Duane
Chief of Engineers (October 11, 1886–June 30, 1888)

James Duane was born June 30, 1824, in Schenectady, New York. His grandfather was a member of the Continental Congress and mayor of New York City. Duane graduated from Union College in 1844 and from the Military Academy in 1848, where he ranked third in his class. He taught practical military engineering there (1852–54) during the superintendency of

Robert E. Lee. Serving with the Army's company of sappers, miners, and pontoniers for nine years before the Civil War, he led its celebrated 1,100-mile march to Utah in 1858 and commanded select engineer troops to guard President Lincoln at his inauguration in 1861. Duane built the

first military ponton bridge over the Potomac at Harpers Ferry in 1862, served as Chief Engineer of the Army of the Potomac (1863–65), and in seven hours in 1864 built the longest ponton bridge of the Civil War (2,170 feet) across the James River. He commanded at Willets Point, New York (1866–68), and for ten years constructed fortifications along the coasts of Maine and New Hampshire. He was president of the Board of Engineers in 1884–86. Appointed Chief of Engineers in 1886, he retired in 1888. He then became Commissioner of Croton Aqueduct, New York. He published a paper on the "History of the Bridge Equipage in the United States Army." General Duane died December 8, 1897, in New York City.

Brigadier General Thomas Lincoln Casey
Chief of Engineers
(July 6, 1888–May 10, 1895)

Thomas Casey was born May 10, 1831, in Sackets Harbor, New York, where his father, Lieutenant Silas Casey (later assault team leader in the battle of Chapultepec in the Mexican War and a general in the Civil War) was then assigned. Young Casey graduated first in the Military Academy class of 1852 and taught engineering there (1854–59).

During the Civil War he oversaw Maine coastal fortifications, completing the massive Fort Knox on the Penobscot River. After that war he headed the division in the Office of the Chief of Engineers responsible for engineer troops, equipment, and fortifications. The Corps' most distinguished builder of monuments and public buildings, Casey headed the Office of Public Buildings and Grounds, District of Columbia, from 1877 to 1881. He built the State, War, and Navy Department Building, which is now the Old Executive Office Building, and completed the Washington Monument. The placing of a sturdier foundation under the partially completed Washington Monument (already 173 feet high) was Casey's greatest engineering feat, but his crowning accomplishment was construction of the Library of Congress building—all but completed when he died suddenly on March 25, 1896. Burial was at the Casey farm in Rhode Island. General Casey was a member of the National Academy of Sciences and the Society of the Cincinnati and an officer of the Legion of Honor of France.

Brigadier General William Price Craighill
Chief of Engineers
(May 10, 1895–February 1, 1897)

William Craighill was born on July 1, 1833, in Charles Town, Virginia (now West Virginia). A classmate of Sheridan, Hood, and McPherson, he ranked second in the Military Academy class of

1853 and was commissioned in the Corps of Engineers. After working on several Atlantic coast forts, he taught engineering at the Military Academy in 1859–62. Another Virginian who stood for the Union, Craighill was division and department engineer during the Civil War and worked on the defenses of Pittsburgh, Baltimore, San Francisco, and New York. After that war, he superintended construction of defenses at Baltimore Harbor and Hampton Roads. He headed the Engineer Office in Baltimore from 1870 to 1895, overseeing river and harbor work in Maryland and parts of Virginia and North Carolina. When the Corps began to build locks and dams on the Great Kanawha River in West Virginia in 1875, Craighill assumed charge there as well. He completed the first of the moveable wicket dams built in the United States, after visiting France to study their use. He became the Corps' first Southeast Division Engineer. Craighill established the camp for the Yorktown surrender celebration, the first of the sanitary type later adapted

to Army camps. He was a member of the Board of Engineers in 1886–89. He was appointed Chief of Engineers by President Cleveland in 1895. He retired two years later and died January 18, 1909, in Charles Town, West Virginia.

Brigadier General John Moulder Wilson
Chief of Engineers
(February 1, 1897–April 30, 1901)

John Wilson was born October 8, 1837, in Washington,

D.C. He graduated from the Military Academy in 1860 and was commissioned in the Artillery Corps. He transferred to the Corps of Topographical Engineers in July 1862 and was awarded the Medal of Honor for fighting at Malvern Hill, Virginia, on August 6, 1862. He joined the Corps

of Engineers in 1863 and received three brevets for gallant service in Alabama. After the Civil War, Wilson worked on Hudson River improvements and drafted plans for the canal around the Cascades of the Columbia River. He improved the Great Lakes harbors of Oswego, Cleveland, and Toledo. Wilson headed the divisions of the Chief's office pertaining to military affairs for four years, was in charge of public buildings and grounds in Washington during both Cleveland administrations, and was Superintendent of the Military Academy in 1889–93. Before his appointment as Chief of Engineers, he was Northeast Division Engineer. As Chief of Engineers, he directed the Corps' activities during the Spanish–American War. He retired April 30, 1901, but remained a prominent figure in the cultural life of Washington until his death there on February 1, 1919.

Brigadier General Henry M. Robert
Chief of Engineers
(April 30, 1901–May 2, 1901)

Born May 2, 1837, in South Carolina, Henry Robert graduated fourth in the Military Academy class of 1857. After receiving his commission in the Corps of Engineers, he taught at the Military Academy

and then explored routes for wagon roads in the West and engaged in fortification work in Puget Sound. During the Civil War he worked on the defenses of Washington and Philadelphia. Robert served as Engineer of the Army's Division of the Pacific in 1867–71. He then spent two years improving rivers in Oregon and Washington and six years developing the harbors of Green Bay and other northern Wisconsin and Michigan ports. He subsequently improved the harbors of Oswego, Philadelphia, and Long Island Sound and constructed locks and dams on the Cumberland and Tennessee rivers. As Southwest Division Engineer from 1897 to 1901, Robert studied how to deepen the Southwest Pass of the Mississippi River. Robert was president of the Board of Engineers from 1895 to 1901. He was made brigadier general on April 30, 1901, and was appointed Chief of Engineers. He served until May 2, 1901, when he retired from the Army. He died May 1, 1923, in Hornell, New York. He became famous for his *Pocket Manual of Rules of Order,* a compendium of parliamentary law first published in 1876 and better known today as *Robert's Rules of Order.*

Brigadier General John W. Barlow
Chief of Engineers
(May 2, 1901–May 3, 1901)

John Barlow was born in New York City on June 26, 1838, and graduated from the Military Academy in May 1861. He was first commissioned in the Artillery Corps, but transferred to the Topographical

Engineers in July 1862. He served with the Battalion of Engineers at Gettysburg and as engineer of an army corps in the siege of Atlanta. He supervised the defenses of Nashville and was brevetted lieutenant colonel for his gallant service there in December 1864. From 1870 until 1874 he was General Sheridan's Chief Engineer in the Military Division of the Missouri. During this period he made scientific explorations of the headwaters of the Missouri

and Yellowstone. His detailed reports became guides for settlers. Barlow improved the harbors and defenses of Long Island Sound from 1875 to 1883, executed harbor improvements in northern Wisconsin and Michigan, and worked on the construction of a canal around Muscle Shoals on the Tennessee River. He was the senior American member of the international commission that re-marked the disputed boundary with Mexico in 1892–96. He was subsequently Northwest Division Engineer for four years. On May 2, 1901, he was commissioned brigadier general and appointed Chief of Engineers. The next day, May 3, 1901, he retired from the Army after 40 years of service. He died February 27, 1914, in Jerusalem, Palestine, at the age of 75.

Brigadier General George Lewis Gillespie, Jr.
Chief of Engineers
(May 3, 1901–January 23, 1904)

George Gillespie, Jr., was born October 7, 1841, in Kingston,

Tennessee. He graduated second in the class of 1862 at the Military Academy and was commissioned in the Corps of Engineers. Another Southerner who remained loyal to the Union, Gillespie joined the Army of the Potomac in September 1862. He commanded two companies of the engineer battalion that built fortifications and ponton bridges throughout the Virginia campaigns until the Appomattox surrender. He received the Medal of Honor for carrying dispatches through enemy lines under withering fire to General Sheridan at Cold Harbor, Virginia. He was later Sheridan's Chief Engineer in the Army of the Shenandoah and the Military Division of the Gulf. After the Civil War Gillespie successively supervised the improvement of harbors at Cleveland, Chicago, Boston, and New York. He initiated construction of the canal at the Cascades of the Columbia River and built the famous lighthouse on Tillamook Rock off the Oregon coast. Gillespie also served on the Board of Engineers and for six years as president of the Mississippi River Commission. He commanded the Army's Department of the East in 1898. While Chief of

Engineers, he was acting Secretary of War in August 1901. He had charge of ceremonies at President McKinley's funeral and at the laying of the cornerstone of the War College Building in 1903. He served as Army Assistant Chief of Staff in 1904–05 with the rank of major general. General Gillespie retired June 15, 1905, and died September 27, 1913, in Saratoga Springs, New York.

Brigadier General Alexander Mackenzie
Chief of Engineers
(January 23, 1904–May 25, 1908)

Born May 25, 1844, in Potosi, Wisconsin, Alexander Mackenzie graduated from the

Military Academy in 1864. Commissioned in the Corps of Engineers, he served with the Union Army in Arkansas in 1864–65. Mackenzie spent six years commanding a company of engineer troops at Willets Point, New York, that experimented in the use of torpedoes in coastal defense. In 1879 he began a 16-year stint as Rock Island District Engineer. He built 100 miles of wing dams on the upper Mississippi River and produced a $4\frac{1}{2}$-foot channel between St. Paul and the mouth of the Missouri River. Called to Washington in 1895, he became Assistant to the Chief of Engineers in charge of all matters relating to river and harbor improvements. He was a member of the general staff corps and War College Board when appointed Chief of Engineers. Retired May 25, 1908, as a major general, he was recalled to active duty in 1917 at age 73 as Northwest Division Engineer serving again in Rock Island, Illinois. General Mackenzie died March 21, 1921, in Washington, D.C.

Brigadier General William Louis Marshall
Chief of Engineers
(July 2, 1908–June 11, 1910)

William Marshall was born June 11, 1846, in Washington,

Kentucky, a scion of the family of Chief Justice John Marshall. At age 16 he enlisted in the 10th Kentucky Cavalry, Union Army. He graduated from the Military Academy in 1868 and was commissioned in the Corps of Engineers. Accompanying Lieutenant George Wheeler's Expedition (1872–76), Marshall covered thousands of miles on foot and horseback and discovered Marshall Pass in central Colorado. He oversaw improvements on the lower Mississippi River near Vicksburg and on the Fox River canal system in Wisconsin. As Chicago District Engineer from 1888 to 1899, he planned and began to build the Illinois and Mississippi Canal. Marshall made innovative use of concrete masonry and developed original and cost-saving methods of lock canal construction. Stationed at New York (1900–08), his genius further expressed itself on the Ambrose Channel project and in fortification construction. He retired June 11, 1910, but his engineering reputation earned a special appointment from President Taft as consulting engineer to the Secretary of the Interior on hydroelectric power projects. General Marshall died July 2, 1920, in Washington, D.C.

Brigadier General William Herbert Bixby
Chief of Engineers
(June 12, 1910–August 11, 1913)

Born December 27, 1849, in Charlestown, Massachusetts, William Bixby graduated first

in the Military Academy class of 1873 and was commissioned in the Corps of Engineers. After serving with the engineer battalion at Willets Point and as Assistant Professor of Engineering at the Military Academy, Bixby graduated with honors from the French *Ecole des ponts et chaussées*. He received the Order, Legion of Honor, for assisting French Army maneuvers. Bixby headed the Wilmington, North Carolina, District from 1884 to 1891. He oversaw improvements on the Cape Fear River, modernized the area's coastal forts, and responded to the earthquake that hit Charleston, South Carolina, in 1886. Bixby served next as District Engineer in Newport, Rhode Island. From 1897 to 1902 he oversaw improvements on the Ohio River and its tributaries from Pittsburgh to Cincinnati. After two years in charge of the Detroit District, he became Chicago District Engineer and Northwest Division Engineer. Bixby was president of the Mississippi River Commission in 1908–10 and 1917–18. As Chief of Engineers, he

oversaw the raising of the battleship *Maine*. He retired August 11, 1913, but was recalled to service in 1917 as Western Division Engineer. He died September 29, 1928, in Washington, D.C.

Brigadier General William Trent Rossell
Chief of Engineers
(August 12, 1913–October 11, 1913)

William Rossell was born in Alabama on October 11, 1849, the son and grandson of Army officers, and he gradu-

ated third in the Military Academy class of 1873. Commissioned in the Corps of Engineers, he served until 1880 at Willets Point and as

Assistant Professor of Engineering at the Military Academy. He then engaged in river, harbor, and fortification work in regions around Portland, Maine; Jacksonville, Florida; and Vicksburg, Mississippi. Rossell served in 1891–93 as the Engineer Commissioner on the three-member governing board of the District of Columbia. After briefly commanding the Battalion of Engineers, he led Mobile District for six years. He then supervised lighthouse construction and repair in the New York area and, later, Ohio River improvements. He was a member of the Mississippi River Commission from 1906 to 1913, as well as Central Division Engineer in 1908–09 and Eastern Division Engineer in 1909–13. He retired October 11, 1913, but was recalled to active service in 1917. He led the Third New York and Puerto Rico districts and was Northeast Division Engineer. He again retired in 1918. He died October 11, 1919, in Staten Island, New York.

Brigadier General Dan Christie Kingman
Chief of Engineers
(October 12, 1913–March 6, 1916)

Born March 6, 1852, in Dover, New Hampshire, Dan Kingman graduated second in the Military Academy class of 1875 and was commissioned in the Corps of Engineers. He served as an instructor at the Military Academy and as the engineer officer of the Army's

Department of the Platte. In 1883 he also began the construction of roads and bridges in the new Yellowstone National Park. Kingman directed improvements along the lower Mississippi River in 1886–90 and received the thanks of the Louisiana legislature for "splendid service rendered" during the 1890 flood. He oversaw harbor and fortification work on Lake Ontario in 1891–95 and improvements on the Tennessee River in the last half of that decade. In the

latter assignment he initiated planning for federal cost-sharing with private hydroelectric-power investors for a lock and dam built below Chattanooga. Kingman oversaw substantial harbor improvements at Cleveland in 1901–05 and headed the Corps' Savannah District and Southeast Division in 1906–13. The Panama Canal was completed while he was Chief of Engineers. He retired March 6, 1916, and died November 14, 1916, in Atlantic City, New Jersey. General Kingman was buried with high military honors in Arlington National Cemetery. Among the pallbearers were Chief of Staff General Hugh L. Scott and two former Chiefs of Engineers, Generals Mackenzie and Bixby.

Major General William Murray Black
Chief of Engineers
(March 7, 1916–October 31, 1919)

Born December 8, 1855, in Lancaster, Pennsylvania, William Black graduated first in the Military Academy class of 1877 and was commissioned

in the Corps of Engineers. From 1886 to 1891 Black headed the Jacksonville District, and in 1897–98 he was the Engineer Commissioner on the governing board of the District of Columbia. In the Spanish–American War, he was Chief Engineer, 3d and 5th Army Corps. As Chief Engineer under Generals William Ludlow and Leonard Wood (1899–1901), and six years later as advisor to the Cuban Department of Public Works, he modernized Havana's sanitary system. As Commandant of the Army Engineer School (1901–03), Black moved it from Willets Point, New York, to Washington Barracks, D.C. After his return from Cuba in 1909, he was Northeast Division Engineer and chairman of a board to raise the battleship *Maine*. Devoted to training young engineer officers in the art of war, General Black's greatest responsibility came as Chief of Engineers during World War I in mobilizing and training some 300,000 engineer troops for a wide range of military engineering tasks. For this work he was awarded the Distinguished Service Medal. He retired October 31, 1919, and died September 24, 1933, in Washington, D.C.

Major General Lansing Hoskins Beach
Chief of Engineers (February 10, 1920–June 18, 1924)

Born June 18, 1860, in Dubuque, Iowa, Lansing Beach graduated third in the Military Academy class of 1882 and was commissioned in the Corps of Engineers. He developed plans for the reconstruction of the Muskingum

River locks and dams soon after Ohio ceded the state-built improvements to the federal government in 1887. From 1894 to 1901 he worked on public improvements in the District of Columbia, serving as Engineer Commissioner there in 1898–1901. As Detroit District Engineer in 1901–05, he oversaw harbor improvements as far west as Duluth. Beach supervised improvements along the Louisiana Gulf coast in 1908–12 and in Baltimore in 1912–15. He also oversaw the entire Gulf Division in six of those seven years and the Central Division in 1915–20. In the latter capacity and as Chief of Engineers, he oversaw construction of the huge Wilson Locks and Dam on the Tennessee River. Beach also served on the Mississippi River Commission and the Board of Engineers for Rivers and Harbors. After his four-year tour as Chief of Engineers, he retired on June 18, 1924. After retirement, General Beach served as consulting engineer for various business interests in the United States and Mexico. He was

president, American Society of Military Engineers, and a member of the International Water Commission from 1924 to 1930. He died April 2, 1945, in Pasadena, California.

Major General Harry Taylor
Chief of Engineers (June 19, 1924–June 26, 1926)

Born June 26, 1862, in Tilton, New Hampshire, Harry Taylor graduated from the Military Academy in 1884 and was commissioned in the Corps of

Engineers. After serving in engineer offices in Wilmington, North Carolina, and New York City, Taylor served from 1891 to 1900 on fortifications and river and harbor construction work in Oregon and Washington. Later he pursued similar work in New England and New York. Transferred to the Philippines, he supervised all fortification

work there in 1904–05. Taylor was district engineer in New London, Connecticut, in 1906–11. He then headed the River and Harbor Division in the Office of the Chief of Engineers for five years. During World War I he served as Chief Engineer, American Expeditionary Forces in France (mid-1917 to mid-1918), and received the Distinguished Service Medal. He then served for six years as Assistant Chief of Engineers, before assuming the top office in the Corps. Wilson Dam was completed while he was Chief. He was a member of the French Legion of Honor. General Taylor retired June 26, 1926. He died January 27, 1930, in Washington, D.C., and was buried in Arlington National Cemetery.

Major General Edgar Jadwin
Chief of Engineers (June 27, 1926–August 7, 1929)

Born August 7, 1865, in Honesdale, Pennsylvania, Edgar Jadwin graduated first in the Military Academy class of 1890 and was commissioned in the Corps of Engineers. He served with engineer troops in 1891–95 and was lieutenant colonel of the 3d U.S. Volunteer Engineers in the Spanish–American War.

After serving as district engineer at the expanding ports of Los Angeles and Galveston, he was selected by General Goethals as an assistant in the construction of the Panama Canal. Jadwin served in 1911–16 in the Office of the Chief of Engineers focusing on bridge and road matters. Upon the United States' entry into World War I in 1917, he recruited the 15th Engineers, a railway construction regiment, and led it to France. He directed American construction and forestry work there for a year and received the Distinguished Service Medal. President Wilson appointed Jadwin to investigate conditions in Poland in 1919. In 1922–24 Jadwin headed the Corps' Charleston District and

Southeast Division. He then served two years as Assistant Chief of Engineers. As Chief of Engineers he sponsored the plan for Mississippi River flood control that was adopted by Congress in May 1928. Jadwin retired as a lieutenant general, August 7, 1929. He died in Gorgas Hospital in the Canal Zone on March 2, 1931, and was buried in Arlington National Cemetery with full military honors.

Major General Lytle Brown
Chief of Engineers (October 1, 1929–October 1, 1933)

Born November 22, 1872, in Nashville, Tennessee, Lytle Brown graduated fourth in the Military Academy class of

1898 and was commissioned in the Corps of Engineers. He served with engineer troops in Cuba in 1898 at the Battle of San Juan Hill and the siege of Santiago and in 1900–02 was Engineer of the Department of Northern Luzon in the Philippine Islands. Brown oversaw river improvement projects in 1908–12 as Louisville District Engineer. He commanded the 2d Battalion of Engineers and served as engineer of Pershing's 1916 punitive expedition into Mexico. Brown headed the War Plans Division of the War Department General Staff from May

1918 to June 1919, addressing important Army policy issues during and immediately after World War I. He received a Distinguished Service Medal. Brown oversaw construction work at the Wilson Dam hydroelectric project in 1919–20. He was assistant commandant of the Army War College and a brigade commander in the Canal Zone before becoming Chief of Engineers. He concluded his military career as commander of the Panama Canal Department (1935–36). General Brown retired November 30, 1936. He died in Nashville, Tennessee, on May 3, 1951.

Major General Edward Murphy Markham
*Chief of Engineers
(October 1, 1933–October 18, 1937)*

Born July 6, 1877, in Troy, New York, Edward Markham graduated fifth in the Military Academy class of 1899 and was commissioned in the Corps of Engineers. He served five years with the 2d Battalion of

Engineers, including two years in the Philippines and eight months in Cuba, engaging in military mapping and road and bridge construction. He was Memphis District Engineer (1912–16) and Professor of Practical Military Engineering at the Military Academy. He served in France during

World War I as Deputy Director, Division of Light Railways and Roads (1918), and in Germany as Chief Engineer, Third Army (1919). After returning to the United States, he was Detroit District Engineer (1919–25) and Commandant of the Army Engineer School, Fort Humphreys, Virginia. He then served as Great Lakes Division Engineer. After serving as Chief of Engineers, he made a special military survey in the Hawaiian Islands. General Markham retired February 28, 1938. He was New York Public Works Commissioner in 1938 and President, Great Lakes Dredge & Dock Company, in Chicago from 1938 to 1945. He died September 14, 1950.

Major General Julian Larcombe Schley
*Chief of Engineers
(October 18, 1937–October 1, 1941)*

Born February 23, 1880, in Savannah, Georgia, Julian Schley graduated from the Military Academy in 1903 and was commissioned in the Corps of Engineers. He and classmate Douglas MacArthur had their first service with the 3d Battalion of Engineers in the Philippines (1903–04). Schley later

served with engineer troops in the United States and Cuba; as an instructor at the Military Academy; as Assistant Engineer, Washington, D.C.; and as New Orleans District Engineer. During World War I he commanded the divisional 307th Engineers in the St. Mihiel and Meuse–Argonne offensives and was Engineer, 5th Army Corps, during the last two weeks of the latter drive. He received a Distinguished Service Medal. He was Director of Purchase, General Staff, and a member of the War Department Claims Board in 1919–20. Schley later served four-year tours as Galveston District Engineer; Engineer of Maintenance, Panama Canal; and Governor of the Canal Zone. In the last post he was also

military advisor to the Republic of Panama. Schley was Commandant of the Army Engineer School in 1936–37. He retired September 30, 1941, but was recalled to active wartime duty in 1943 as Director of Transportation, Office of the Coordinator of Inter-American Affairs. He died March 29, 1965, in Washington, D.C.

Lieutenant General Eugene Reybold
*Chief of Engineers
(October 1, 1941–September 30, 1945)*

Born February 13, 1884, in Delaware City, Delaware, Eugene Reybold was distinguished as the World War II Chief of Engineers who directed the largest Corps of Engineers in the nation's history.

He graduated from Delaware College in 1903. Commissioned in the Coast Artillery Corps in 1908, Reybold was assigned to military housing and coast defense construction work. Stationed at Fort Monroe throughout World War I, he became commandant of the Coast Artillery School. He

transferred to the Corps of Engineers in 1926 and served as District Engineer in Buffalo, New York; Wilmington, North Carolina; and Memphis, Tennessee. In the last assignment he successfully battled record Mississippi River flood crests. He was Southwestern Division Engineer (1937–40) and War Department Assistant Chief of Staff, G–4 (1940–41). Appointed Chief of Engineers shortly before Pearl Harbor, General Reybold directed the Corps' tremendous range of activities throughout the war and was the first officer ever to rank as lieutenant general while Chief of Engineers. He was awarded a Distinguished Service Medal with Oak Leaf Cluster. Reybold retired January 31, 1946, and died November 21, 1961, in Washington, D.C.

Lieutenant General Raymond A. Wheeler
*Chief of Engineers
(October 4, 1945–February 28, 1949)*

Born July 31, 1885, in Peoria, Illinois, Raymond Wheeler graduated fifth in the Military Academy class of 1911 and

was commissioned in the Corps of Engineers. He served with the Veracruz Expedition in 1914 and went to France with the divisional 4th Engineers in 1918. He was awarded a Silver Star for actions in the Aisne–Marne campaign and by the end of World War I had assumed command of his regiment with the rank of colonel. Between the two world wars he served as District Engineer in Newport, Rhode Island; Wilmington, North Carolina; and Rock Island, Illinois. In September 1941 he was appointed chief of the U.S. Military Iranian Mission and in February 1942 was transferred to the China–Burma–India Theater as Commanding General of the Services of Supply. In October 1943 he was assigned to Lord Mountbatten's Southeast Asia Command as principal administrative officer and Deputy Supreme Commander. Before the end of World War II, he became Commander of the India–Burma Theater. He represented the United States at the Japanese surrender in Singapore. As Chief of Engineers, Wheeler initiated construction of the Missouri River dams projected in the Pick–Sloan Plan. After his military retirement, he worked for the United Nations and the International Bank for Reconstruction and Development on Asian and African development projects. He oversaw the clearing of the Suez Canal in 1956–57. He died February 8, 1974, in Washington, D.C. Wheeler's U.S. Army decorations included the Distinguished Service Medal with two Oak Leaf Clusters and the Legion of Merit. He was also made an honorary knight of the British Empire.

Lieutenant General Lewis A. Pick
Chief of Engineers
(March 1, 1949–January 26, 1953)

Born in Brookneal, Virginia, November 18, 1890, Lewis Pick graduated from Virginia Polytechnic Institute in 1914. During World War I he served with the 23d Engineers in France. Pick received his Regular Army commission in the Corps of Engineers on July 1, 1920. He served in the Philippines from 1921 until 1923 and helped organize an engineer regiment composed of Filipino soldiers. He was District Engineer at New Orleans during the great 1927 Mississippi River floods, and he helped coordinate federal relief efforts. Pick was named Missouri River Division Engineer in 1942, and with W. Glenn Sloan of the Bureau of Reclamation he co-wrote the Pick–Sloan Plan for controlling the water resources of the Missouri River Basin. Pick was assigned to the China–Burma–India Theater of Operations in October 1943 and oversaw the construction of the Ledo Road across northern Burma from India to China. After his return to the United States in 1945, he served again as Missouri River Division Engineer. On March 1, 1949, President Truman appointed him Chief of Engineers. Pick was awarded the Distinguished Service Medal with Oak Leaf Cluster. He died December 2, 1956, in Washington, D.C.

Lieutenant General Samuel D. Sturgis, Jr.
Chief of Engineers
(March 17, 1953–September 30, 1956)

Born July 16, 1897, in St. Paul, Minnesota, Samuel Sturgis, Jr., came from an illustrious military family. Both his father and grandfather were Military Academy graduates and major generals. Young Sturgis graduated from the Military Academy in 1918. As a junior engineer officer

he taught mathematics at the academy for four years. In 1926 he was ordered to the Philippines, where he served as Adjutant of the 14th Engineers. His strategical studies of the islands over a three-year period developed knowledge he used later when he returned to the Philippines in 1944 as Chief Engineer of General Walter Krueger's Sixth Army. Sturgis commanded a mounted engineer company at Fort Riley, Kansas, in 1929–33 and encouraged the adoption of heavy mechanical equipment. He was District Engineer in 1939–42 in Vicksburg, Mississippi, where he worked on flood control and a large military construction program. In 1943–45 Sturgis' engineer troops built roads, airfields, ports, and bases from New Guinea to the Philippines. Sturgis was senior engineer for the nation's air forces in 1946–48 and was Missouri River Division Engineer in 1949–51. In 1951 he became the Commanding General of the 6th Armored Division and Fort Leonard Wood. In 1952 he was appointed Commanding General of the Communications Zone

supporting the United States Army in Europe. He became Chief of Engineers on March 17, 1953. His military decorations included the Distinguished Service Medal with Oak Leaf Cluster, Silver Star, Legion of Merit, and Bronze Star Medal. He died July 5, 1964, in Washington, D.C.

Lieutenant General Emerson C. Itschner
Chief of Engineers
(October 1, 1956–March 27, 1961)

Born in Chicago, Illinois, July 1, 1903, Emerson Itschner graduated from the Military Academy in 1924 and was commissioned in the Corps of Engineers. He obtained a degree in civil engineering from Cornell University in 1926. Itschner served with the Alaska Road Commission in 1927–29. He taught at the Missouri School of Mines and

served as assistant to the Upper Mississippi Valley Division Engineer and the St. Louis District Engineer. He commanded a topographic survey company in 1940–41. In 1942–43 Itschner headed the office in Corps headquarters that supervised Army airfield construction in the 48 states. In 1944–45 he oversaw the reconstruction of ports and the development of supply routes to U.S. forces in Europe as Engineer, Advance Section, Communications Zone. Itschner headed the division in Corps headquarters responsible for military construction operations from

1946 to 1949. After a year as Seattle District Engineer, he went to Korea as Engineer of I Corps and oversaw engineer troop operations in western Korea. He was North Pacific Division Engineer in 1952–53. From 1953 until being appointed Chief of Engineers, he served as Assistant Chief of Engineers for Civil Works. He was awarded the Distinguished Service Medal, Legion of Merit with two Oak Leaf Clusters, Bronze Star Medal, and Purple Heart. General Itschner retired in 1961 and died in 1995.

Lieutenant General Walter K. Wilson, Jr.
Chief of Engineers
(May 19, 1961–June 30, 1965)

The son of an artillery officer, Walter Wilson, Jr., was born at Fort Barrancas, Florida, on August 26, 1906. He graduated from the Military Academy in 1929 and was commissioned in the Corps of Engineers. Before 1942 he served with troops, continued his military and engineering education, and was an instructor at the Military Academy. During World War II Wilson served as Deputy Engineer-in-Chief with the Southeast Asia Command at New Delhi, India, and Kandy, Ceylon. He became Commanding General, Advance Section, U.S. Forces, India–Burma Theater, and Chief of Staff of the Chinese Army in India. Later, he commanded Intermediate and Base Sections and consolidated all three, commanding all ground forces remaining in the theater. He was District Engineer in St. Paul, Minnesota (1946–49), and Mobile, Alabama (1949–52), and then South Atlantic (1952–53) and Mediterranean Division Engineer (1953–55). He assumed command of the 18th Engineer Brigade at Fort Leonard Wood, Missouri, in 1955. He served as Deputy Chief of Engineers for Construction from 1956 to 1960. Wilson was Commanding General of the Army Engineer Center and Fort Belvoir and Commandant of the Army Engineer School

in 1960–61. He retired as Chief of Engineers on June 30, 1965. Wilson's military honors included the Legion of Merit with Oak Leaf Cluster, the Soldier's Medal, and membership in the French Legion of Honor. He died in Mobile, Alabama, on December 6, 1985.

Lieutenant General William F. Cassidy
Chief of Engineers
(July 1, 1965–July 31, 1969)

Born on an Army post near Nome, Alaska, on August 28, 1908, William Cassidy graduated from the Military Academy in 1931, and was commissioned in the Corps of Engineers. He served as assistant to the District Engineer in Portland, Oregon; commanded an engineer company at Fort Belvoir, Virginia; and

oversaw military construction projects in Hawaii. During World War II Cassidy commanded engineer troops specializing in airfield construction in England, North Africa, and Italy. He was Deputy Chief, then Chief, War Plans (later Operations and Training) Division, Office of the

Chief of Engineers, in 1944–47. At the outbreak of the Korean conflict, he was ordered to Japan where he was responsible for engineer supply. He served as South Pacific Division Engineer from 1955 to 1958 and was the senior logistics advisor to the Republic of Korea Army in 1958–59. Cassidy was the Corps' Director of Civil Works from September 1959 to March 1962 and was then appointed Deputy Chief of Engineers. On March 1, 1963, he became the Commanding General of the Army Engineer Center and Fort Belvoir and Commandant of the Army Engineer School. Cassidy became Chief of Engineers on July 1, 1965. He was awarded the Distinguished Service Medal for his service as Chief of Engineers. His other military decorations included the Legion of Merit with Oak Leaf Cluster, the Bronze Star Medal, and the Republic of Korea Presidential Citation.

Lieutenant General Frederick J. Clarke
Chief of Engineers
(August 1, 1969–July 31, 1973)

Born in Little Falls, New York, on March 1, 1915, Frederick Clarke was commissioned in the Corps of Engineers in 1937 after graduating fourth in his Military Academy class. Clarke received a master's degree in civil engineering from Cornell University in 1940 and later attended the Advanced Management Program of the Graduate School of Business, Harvard University. During World War II he commanded a battalion that helped construct a military airfield on Ascension Island in the South Atlantic, and he served in Washington, D.C., with Headquarters, Army Service Forces. After the war Clarke worked in the atomic energy field for the Manhattan District and the

Atomic Energy Commission at Hanford, Washington, and at the Armed Forces Special Weapons Project at Sandia Base, Albuquerque, New Mexico. As the District Engineer of the Trans-East District of the Corps in 1957–59, he was responsible for U.S. military construction in Pakistan and Saudi Arabia, and he initiated transportation surveys in East Pakistan and Burma. In the decade before his appoint-

ment as Chief of Engineers, Clarke was Engineer Commissioner of the District of Columbia (1960–63); Director of Military Construction in the Office of the Chief of Engineers (1963–65); Commanding General of the Army Engineer Center and Fort Belvoir and Commandant of the Army Engineer School (1965–66); and Deputy Chief of Engineers (1966–69). As Chief of Engineers Clarke guided the Corps as it devoted increased attention to the environmental impact of its work. General Clarke was awarded the Distinguished Service Medal and the Legion of Merit.

Lieutenant General William C. Gribble, Jr.
Chief of Engineers
(August 1, 1973–June 30, 1976)

Born in Ironwood, Michigan, on May 24, 1917, William Gribble, Jr., graduated from the Military Academy in 1941 and was commissioned in the

150

Corps of Engineers. During World War II he served on the staff of the 340th Engineer General Service Regiment as it first built a section of the Alaska Highway in western Canada and later assisted MacArthur's drive in New Guinea and the Philippines. At the end of the war he commanded the 118th Engineer Combat Battalion, 43d Infantry Division. Gribble then worked in the Los Alamos laboratory and in the Reactor Development Division of the Atomic Energy Commission. As Alaska District Engineer he oversaw construction of a nuclear power plant at Fort Greely, Alaska. He headed the Army's nuclear power program in 1960–61. In 1963 he was the Corps' North Central Division Engineer. Gribble's scientific skills led to his service as Director of Research and Development in the Army Materiel Command in 1964–66 and as the Army's Chief of Research and Development in 1971–73. In 1969–70 he commanded the Army Engineer Center and Fort Belvoir and was Commandant of the Army Engineer School. He became Chief of Engineers in 1973. Gribble received a master's degree in physical science from the University of Chicago in 1948 and an honorary doctorate in engineering from Michigan Technological University. He was also an honorary member of the United Kingdom's Institute of Royal Engineers. His decorations included the Distinguished Service Medal with Oak Leaf Cluster, the Legion of Merit with Oak Leaf Cluster, and the Brazilian Order of Military Merit. General Gribble died at Fort Belvoir, Virginia, on June 2, 1979.

Lieutenant General John W. Morris
Chief of Engineers (July 1, 1976–September 30, 1980)

John Morris was born in Princess Anne, Maryland, on September 10, 1921. He graduated from the Military Academy in June 1943 and was commissioned in the Corps of Engineers. During World War II he commanded an airfield construction company in the Western Pacific. After the war he served in the Philippines and Japan, in the Corps' Savannah District, and as area engineer at Goose Bay, Labrador. In 1960–62 he commanded the divisional 8th Engineer Battalion in Korea. Morris headed the Corps' Tulsa District in 1962–65 as it improved navigation on the Arkansas River. During the peak years of the Vietnam War, he was the Army's Deputy Chief of Legislative Liaison (1967–69), and he commanded the 18th Engineer Brigade in Vietnam (1969–70).

He was then Missouri River Division Engineer for two years, the Corps' Director of Civil Works for three years, and Deputy Chief of Engineers in 1975–76. As Chief of Engineers, Morris convinced the Army to include the Corps of Engineers among its major commands. Morris obtained a master's degree in civil engineering from the University of Iowa. His military awards included the Distinguished Service Medal, the Legion of Merit with three Oak Leaf Clusters, the Bronze Star Medal, and the Defense Meritorious Service Medal. General Morris was selected Construction's Man of the Year for 1977 by the *Engineering-News Record*.

Lieutenant General Joseph K. Bratton
Chief of Engineers (October 1, 1980–September 14, 1984)

Joseph Bratton was born on April 4, 1926, in St. Paul, Minnesota. He graduated third in the class of 1948 at the Military Academy and was commissioned in the Corps of Engineers. He

served with an engineer battalion in Austria in 1949–52 and with the divisional 13th Engineer Combat Battalion in Korea in 1953–54, both before and after the armistice. He later commanded the 24th Engineer Battalion, 4th Armored Division, in Germany (1964–65) and the 159th Engineer Group in Vietnam (1969–70). Bratton also held numerous staff assignments. He was a military assistant to Secretary of the Army Stanley Resor in 1967–69 and Secretary to the Joint Chiefs of Staff in 1970–72. Having received a master's degree in nuclear engineering from the Massachusetts Institute of Technology in 1959, Bratton served as Chief of Nuclear Activities, Supreme Headquarters, Allied Powers, Europe (SHAPE), in 1972–75 and Director of Military Applications at the U.S. Department of Energy in 1975–79. His last assignments before becoming Chief of Engineers in October 1980 were as Division Engineer of the Corps' South Atlantic Division (1979–80) and then briefly as Deputy Chief of Engineers. His military awards included the Defense Distinguished Service Medal, the Army Distinguished Service Medal, the Legion of Merit with two Oak Leaf Clusters, and the Bronze Star Medal with Oak Leaf Cluster.

Lieutenant General Elvin R. Heiberg III
Chief of Engineers (September 14, 1984–May 5, 1988)

Lieutenant General E. R. Heiberg III was born at Schofield Barracks Honolulu, Hawaii, on March 2, 1932, Elvin Heiberg III became a third-generation West Pointer when he graduated fifth in the Military Academy class of 1953. He later obtained three master's degrees, in civil engineering from the Massachusetts Institute of Technology and in government and administration from George Washington University. Early in his military career Heiberg served as Operations Officer of the 3d Brigade, 3d Infantry Division, in Germany, and taught in the Social Sciences Department at the Military Academy. In 1968–69 he commanded the divisional 4th Engineer Battalion in Vietnam and was awarded a Silver Star. He then served as Special Assistant and Executive Assistant to the Director, Office of Emergency Preparedness, under the Executive Office of the President. Heiberg served for a year as Executive to Secretary of the Army Howard Callaway. He then headed the Corps' New Orleans District and in 1975–78 the Ohio River Division. He served as senior engineer on the staff of U.S. Army, Europe, in 1978–79. Heiberg was the Corps' Director of Civil Works in

1979–82 and then Deputy Chief of Engineers. After managing the Army's Ballistic Missile Defense Program for a year, he became Chief of Engineers in 1984. Heiberg graduated from the Industrial

College of the Armed Forces. His military awards included the Distinguished Service Medal, the Legion of Merit with two Oak Leaf Clusters, the Distinguished Flying Cross, and the Bronze Star Medal.

Lieutenant General Henry J. Hatch

Chief of Engineers
(June 17, 1988–June 4, 1992)

The son of an artillery officer, Henry J. Hatch was born on August 31, 1935, at Pensacola, Florida. After graduating from the U.S. Military Academy in 1957, he completed airborne and ranger training at Fort Benning, Georgia, and took a master's degree in geodetic science at Ohio State University. Hatch held several leadership positions in Army airborne and airmobile units early in his career. He commanded a company of the 82d Airborne Division's 307th Engineer Battalion at Fort Bragg, North Carolina; served on the staff of the 2d Airborne Battle Group, 503d Infantry in Okinawa; and commanded the 326th Engineer Battalion of the 101st Airborne Division in Vietnam in 1968–69.

Hatch subsequently oversaw West Point construction work for the Corps' New York District and in 1974 began a three-year tenure as Nashville District Engineer. He then returned to the Far East to lead the 2d Infantry Division Support Command in Korea and later directed Army and Air Force construction in Korea,

Japan, and the Pacific as Division Engineer of the Corps' Pacific Ocean Division. Hatch was Deputy Chief of Staff, Engineer, for U.S. Army, Europe, in 1981–84. He next returned to the Corps of Engineers, serving briefly as Assistant Chief of Engineers and then for nearly four years as Director of Civil Works. President Reagan nominated him as Chief of Engineers in May 1988. Lieutenant General Hatch has been awarded the Legion of Merit, two Meritorious Service Medals, two Bronze Star Medals, three Air Medals, and two Army Commendation Medals.

Lieutenant General Arthur E. Williams

Chief of Engineers
(August 24, 1992–
June 30, 1996)

Born in Watertown, New York, on March 28, 1938, Arthur Williams obtained a commission as an Army engineer officer upon his graduation in 1960 from Saint Lawrence University, where he majored in mathematics. He later obtained a bachelor's degree in civil engineering from Rensselaer Polytechnic Institute and a master's degree in civil engineering and economic planning from Stanford University. Williams commanded an armored engineer company in Germany and an engineer construction company in Vietnam. During a second tour in Vietnam, he served as Operations Officer of the 577th Engineer Battalion. He later commanded the 44th Engineer Battalion in Korea and was an assignment

officer at the U.S. Army Military Personnel Center. Williams headed the Corps' Sacramento District in 1982–1985 and then served as Chief of Staff at Corps Headquarters. He subsequently headed the Pacific Ocean Division and then the Lower Mississippi Valley Division. He was also President of the Mississippi River Commission. He returned to Corps Headquarters in July 1991 as Director of Civil Works. Williams was nominated as Chief of Engineers by President Bush in 1992. His military awards include the Bronze Star (two awards), the Legion of Merit (three awards), the Defense Meritorious Service Medal, and the Army Commendation Medal.

Lieutenant General Joe N. Ballard

Chief of Engineers
(October 1, 1996–)

A native of Oakdale, Louisiana, Lieutenant General Joe N. Ballard was born on March 27, 1942, and graduated from Southern University and A&M College, Baton Rouge, Louisiana, with a degree in electrical engineering. After graduation in 1965, he received a commission in the U.S. Army Corps of Engineers. General Ballard served as a platoon leader in the 84th Engineer Battalion during his first tour of duty in South Vietnam and as a company commander in the 864th Engineer Battalion and as the Chief, Lines of Communication Section in the 18th Engineer Brigade during his second tour. Following assignments with the Fifth U.S. Army and the Recruiting Command, he was Operations Officer and Executive Officer of the 326th Engineer Battalion, 101st Airborne Division. In 1978 he went to South Korea where he served as Operations Officer and later as the Executive Officer on the staff of the U.S. Forces, Korea, Engineer. Following Korea he returned to the Pentagon for duty on the Army Staff as the principal engineer in the Army Energy Office,

Office of the Deputy Chief of Staff, Logistics. In 1982 he moved to another overseas theater as Commander of the 82d Engineer Battalion, 7th Engineer Brigade, in West Germany. Later he became

the Commander of the 18th Engineer Brigade and Assistant Deputy Chief of Staff, Engineer, in Headquarters, U.S. Army Europe. Returning to the United States in 1991, General Ballard began his association with the U.S. Army Engineer School as Assistant Commandant of the Engineer School and Deputy Commanding General of the Engineer Center and Fort Leonard Wood, Missouri. After an assignment as Chief, Total Army Basing Study in the Office of the Chief of Staff of the Army, General Ballard returned to Missouri as Commanding General of the Engineer Center and Fort Leonard Wood. When he was nominated by President William Clinton to be the Chief of Engineers and Commander, U.S. Army Corps of Engineers, he was serving as Chief of Staff, U.S. Army Training and Doctrine Command in Fort Monroe, Virginia. During his career General Ballard earned a master's degree in engineering management from the University of Missouri and graduated from the Engineer Officer Basic and Advanced Courses, the Command and General Staff College, and the Army War College. His military awards include the Distinguished Service Medal, three Legion of Merit awards, two Bronze Star Medals, the Defense Meritorious Service Medal, four Meritorious Service Medals, and two Army Commendation Medals.

Selected Bibliography

I. GENERAL

Abbot, Henry L. *Early Days of the Engineer School of Application. Occasional Paper No. 14*, United States Army Engineer School (Washington, DC, 1904).

Ambrose, Stephen E. *Duty, Honor, Country: A History of West Point* (Baltimore, 1966).

American Public Works Association. *History of Public Works in the United States. 1776–1976*. Edited by Ellis L. Armstrong (Chicago, 1976).

Burr, Edward. *Historical Sketch of the Corps of Engineers, U.S. Army. Occasional Paper No. 71*, United States Army Engineer School (Washington, DC, 1939).

Cosby, Spencer. "The Work of the Army in the Construction and Maintenance of Roads." *Professional Memoirs 6* (July–August 1914): 539–48.

Cowdrey, Albert E. *A City for the Nation: The Army Engineers and the Building of Washington, DC, 1798–1967* (Washington, DC, 1979).

Crump, Irving. *Our Army Engineers* (New York, 1954).

Davis, Franklin M., Jr., and Thomas T. Jones. *The U.S. Army Engineers, Fighting Elite* (New York, 1967).

Dunne, David M. "The Engineer School — Past and Present." *The Military Engineer 41* (November–December 1949): 411–16.

Forman, Sidney. *West Point: A History of the United States Military Academy* (New York, 1950).

Jewitt, Henry C. "History of the Corps of Engineers to 1915." *The Military Engineer 14* (November–December 1922): 385–88.

McCullough, David G. *The Path Between the Seas: The Creation of the Panama Canal, 1870–1914* (New York, 1977).

Thompson, Paul W. *What the Citizen Should Know About the Army Engineers* (New York, 1942).

United States Army Engineer School. *History and Traditions of the Corps* (Fort Belvoir, VA, 1953).

II. MILITARY

Abbot, Henry L. *Course of Lectures Upon the Defense of the Sea-Coast of the United States* (New York, 1888).

Beardslee, Clarence G. "Development of Army Camp Planning." *Civil Engineering 12* (September 1942): 489–92.

Bond, P. S. *The Engineer in War, with Special Reference to the Training of the Engineer to Meet the Military Obligations of Citizenship* (New York, 1916).

Browning, Robert S. *Two If By Sea: The Development of American Coastal Defense Policy* (Westport, CT, 1983).

Historical Papers Relating to the Corps of Engineers and to Engineer Troops in the Army. Occasional Paper No. 16, United States Army Engineer School (Washington, DC, 1904).

Leach, Smith S. *Historical Sketch of the First Battalion of Engineers During Its Tour Abroad. Occasional Paper No. 7*, United States Army Engineer School (Washington, DC, 1903).

Lenney, John J. *Caste System in the American Army: A Study of the Corps of Engineers and the West Point System* (New York, 1949).

Lewis, Emanuel Raymond. *Seacoast Fortifications of the United States: An Introductory History* (Washington, DC, 1970).

Ludlow, William. "An Army Engineer's Journal of Custer's Black Hills Expedition, July 2, 1874–August 23, 1874." Edited by Eugene McAndrews. *Journal of the West 13* (January 1974): 78–85.

Nelson, Harold L. "Military Roads for War and Peace, 1791–1836." *Military Affairs 19* (Spring 1955): 1–14.

Pick, Lewis A. *The Corps of Engineers in Peace and War* (Washington, DC, 1949).

Robinson, Willard B. *American Forts: Architectural Form and Function* (Urbana, IL, 1977).

Seville, William P. *Narrative of the March of Co. A, Engineers from Fort Leavenworth, Kansas, to Fort Bridger, Utah, and Return May 6 to October 3, 1858*. Edited by John W. N. Schulz. *Occasional Paper No. 48,*

United States Army Engineer School (Washington, DC, 1912).

Thompson, Paul W. *Engineers in Battle* (Harrisburg, PA, 1942).

Warner, Henry. "The Battalion of Engineers, United States Army." *United Service* New Series 15 (May 1896): 420–26.

Youngberg, G. A. *History of Engineer Troops in the United States Army, 1775–1901. Occasional Paper No. 37,* United States Army Engineer School (Washington, DC, 1910).

1. American Revolution

Guthorn, Peter J. *American Maps and Mapmakers of the Revolution* (Monmouth Beach, NJ, 1966).

Martin, Joseph Plumb. *A Narrative of the Some Adventures, Dangers and Sufferings of a Revolutionary Soldier.* Edited by George F. Scheer (Boston, 1962).

Palmer, Dave Richard. *The River and the Rock: The History of Fortress West Point 1775–1783* (New York, 1969).

Walker, Paul K. "An Engineering Victory: The Siege of Yorktown, 1781." *The Military Engineer* 73 (September–October 1981): 334–37.

Walker, Paul K. *Engineers of Independence: A Documentary History of the Army Engineers in the American Revolution 1775–1783* (Washington, DC, 1981).

2. War of 1812

Cullum, George W. *Campaigns of the War of 1812–15 Against Great Britain, Sketched and Criticized, With Brief Biographies of the American Engineers* (New York, 1879).

Tatum, Howell. *Major Howell Tatum's Journal While Acting Topographical Engineer (1814) to General Jackson.* Edited by John S. Bassett (Northhampton, MA, 1922).

Walker, Charles E. "The Other Good Guys: Army Engineers in the War of 1812." *The Military Engineer* 70 (May–June 1978): 178–183.

3. Mexican War

Beauregard, Pierre G. T. *With Beauregard in Mexico: Mexican War Reminiscences.* Edited by T. Harry Williams (Baton Rouge, 1956).

McClellan, George B. *The Mexican War Diary.* Edited by William S. Myers (Princeton, 1917).

Robinson, William M., Jr. "The Engineer Soldiers in the Mexican War."

The Military Engineer 24 (January–February 1932): 1–8.

Smith, Gustavus W. *Company "A," Corps of Engineers, U.S.A., 1846–'48, in the Mexican War* (Willets Point, NY, 1896).

Traas, Adrian G. *From the Golden Gate to Mexico City. The U.S. Army Topographical Engineers in the Mexican War* (Washington, DC, 1993).

4. Civil War

Barnard, John G. *A Report on the Defenses of Washington* (Washington, DC, 1871).

Barnard, John G., and William F. Barry. *Report of the Engineer and Artillery Operations of the Army of the Potomac from Its Organization to the Close of the Peninsular Campaign* (New York, 1863).

Dear Friends At Home. The Letters and Diary of Thomas James Owen, Fiftieth New York Volunteer Engineer Regiment, during the Civil War. Edited by Dale E. Floyd (Fort Belvoir, VA, 1985).

The Engineer Battalion in the Civil War. Occasional Paper No. 44, United States Army Engineer School (Washington, DC, 1910).

Hotchkiss, Jedediah. *Make Me a Map of the Valley: The Civil War Journal of Stonewall Jackson's Topographer.* Edited by Archie P. McDonald (Dallas, 1973).

Nichols, James L. *Confederate Engineers* (Tuscaloosa, 1957).

Thienel, Philip M. "Engineers in the Union Army, 1861–1865." *The Military Engineer* 47 (January–February 1955): 36–41; (March–April 1955): 110–15.

5. Spanish-American War and Philippine Insurrection

Batemann, C. C. "Military Road-Making in Mindanao." *Journal of the Military Service Institution* 33 (September–October 1903): 190–99.

Bullard, Robert L. "Road Building Among the Moros." *Atlantic Monthly* 92 (December 1903): 818–26.

Caples, W. G. *Report Upon the Construction of the Calamba-Batangas Road, Luzon, Philippine Islands. Occasional Paper No. 5,* United States Army Engineer School (Washington, DC, 1903).

Knauff, Francis H. "Remember the Maine." *The Military Engineer* 47 (May–June 1955): 211–13.

Rees, Thomas H. "The Engineer Battalion of the Fifth Army Corps." *Journal of the Military Service Institution* 24 (January 1899): 74–84.

Sibert, William L. "Military Occupation of Northern Luzon." *Journal of the Military Service Institution* 30 (May 1902): 404–08.

Wooten, W. P. *The Provisional Battalion of Engineers in the Philippines. Occasional Paper No. 42,* United States Army Engineer School (Washington, DC, 1910).

6. Mexican Punitive Expedition

Graves, Ernest. "Road Work on the Punitive Expedition into Mexico." *Professional Memoirs* 9 (November–December 1917): 657–81.

O'Connor, James A. "Road Work in Mexico with the Punitive Expedition." *Professional Memoirs* 9 (May–June 1917): 326–43.

7. World War I

Collins, Francis A. *The Fighting Engineers: The Minute Men of Our Industrial Army* (New York, 1918).

Engineer Department, American Expeditionary Forces. *Historical Report of the Chief Engineer, 1917–1919* (Washington, DC, 1919).

Graves, Ernest. *Construction in War. Lessons Taught by the World War 1917–1919. Occasional Paper No. 64,* United States Army Engineer School (Washington, DC, 1921).

Hendricks, Charles. *Combat and Construction: U.S. Army Engineers in World War I* (Fort Belvoir, VA, 1993).

Parsons, William B. *The American Engineers in France* (New York, 1920).

Schley, Julian A. "Some Notes on the World War." *The Military Engineer* 21 (January–February 1929): 55–68.

Swan, Carroll J. *My Company* (Boston, 1918).

Tomlin, Robert K. *American Engineers Behind the Battle Lines of France* (New York, 1918).

8. World War II

Anders, Leslie. *The Ledo Road* (Norman, OK, 1965).

Beck, Alfred M., Abe Bortz, Charles W. Lynch, Lida Mayo, and Ralph F. Weld. *The Corps of Engineers: The War Against Germany.* United States Army in World War II: The Technical Services (Washington, DC, 1985).

Bowman, Waldo G. *American Military Engineering in Europe, From Normandy to the Rhine* (New York, 1945).

Coll, Blanche D., Jean E. Keith, and Herbert H. Rosenthal. *The Corps of Engineers: Troops and Equipment.* United States Army in World War II: The Technical Services (Washington, DC, 1958).

Dod, Karl C. *The Corps of Engineers: The War Against Japan.* United States Army in World War II: The Technical Services (Washington, DC, 1966).

Fine, Lenore, and Jesse A. Remington. *The Corps of Engineers: Construction in the United States.* United States Army in World War II: The Technical Sevices (Washington, DC, 1972).

Fowle, Barry W., ed. *Builders and Fighters: U.S. Army Engineers in World War II* (Fort Belvoir, VA, 1992).

Fowle, Barry W., and Floyd D. Wright. *The 51st Again: An Engineer Combat Battalion in World War II* (Shippensburg, PA, 1992).

Giles, Henry. *The G. I. Journal of Sergeant Giles* (Boston, 1965).

Giles, Janice Holt. *The Damned Engineers.* 2d ed. (Washington, DC, 1985).

Heavey, William F. *Down Ramp! The Story of the Army Amphibian Engineers* (Washington, DC, 1947).

Jones, Vincent C. *Manhattan: The Army and the Atomic Bomb.* United States Army in World War II: Special Studies (Washington, DC, 1985).

Office of the Chief Engineer, General Headquarters, Army Forces Pacific. *Engineers of the Southwest Pacific, 1941–1945* (8 Volumes, Washington, DC, 1947–1959).

Pergin, Col. David E., with Eric Hammel. *First Across the Rhine: The 291st Engineer Combat Battalion in France, Belgium, and Germany* (New York, 1989).

Twichell, Heath. *Northwest Epic: The Building of the Alaska Highway* (New York, 1992).

Zarish, Joseph M. *The Collapse of the Remagen Bridge* (New York, 1967).

9. Korean War

Farquhar, William R., Jr., and Henry A. Jeffers, Jr. *Bridging the Imjin: Construction of the Libby and Teal Bridges During the Korean War.* Edited by Charles Hendricks (Fort Belvoir, VA, 1989).

Hyzer, Peter C. "Third Engineers in Korea, July–October 1950." *The Military Engineer* 43 (March–April 1951): 101–107.

Hyzer, Peter C. "Third Engineers in Korea, Part II, November 1950–February 1951" and "Part III, March–April 1951." *The Military Engineer* 44 (July–August 1952): 252–254; (September–October 1952): 356–361.

Mann, Frank L. "Operation 'Versatile': Korean Saga of the 2d Engineer Special Brigade." *The Military Engineer* 44 (May–June 1952): 168–173.

Rowny, E. L. "Engineers in the Hungnam Evacuation." *The Military Engineer* 43 (September–October 1951): 315–319.

Strong, Paschal N. "Army Engineers in Korea." *The Military Engineer* 44 (November–December 1952): 405–10.

Westover, John G. *Combat Support in Korea: The United States Army in the Korean Conflict* (Washington, DC, 1955).

10. Vietnam War

Dunn, Carroll H. *Base Development in South Vietnam, 1965–1970* (Washington, DC, 1972).

Malley, Lt. Col. Robert J. "Forward Airfield Construction in Vietnam." *The Military Engineer* 59 (September–October 1967): 318–322.

Ploger, Robert R. *U.S. Army Engineers, 1965–1970* (Washington, DC, 1974).

Stearns, Maj. Henry A., Maj. Rudolph E. Abbott, and Capt. James L. Campbell. "LOC Highway Restoration, Vietnam." *The Military Engineer* 65 (March–April 1973): 84–86.

Yens, 1st Lt. David P., and Capt. John P. Clement III. "Port Construction in Vietnam." *The Military Engineer* 59 (January–February 1967): 20–24.

11. Cold War and After

Grathwol, Robert P., and Donita M. Moorhus. *American Forces in Berlin, 1945–1994: Cold War Outpost* (Washington, DC, 1994).

Hatch, Lt. Gen. Henry J., and Janet A. McDonnell. "Corps of Engineers: Laying the Groundwork for Theater Operations." *Military Review* 72 (March 1992): 2–13.

McDonnell, Janet A. "Rebuilding Kuwait." *Military Review* 73 (July 1993): 50–61.

McDonnell, Janet A. *Supporting the Troops: The U.S. Army Corps of Engineers in the Persian Gulf War* (Alexandria, VA, 1996).

Schubert, Frank N. *Building Air Bases in the Negev. The U.S. Army Corps of Engineers in Israel, 1979–1982* (Washington, DC, 1992).

III. CIVIL WORKS

Arnold, Joseph L. *The Evolution of the Flood Control Act of 1936* (Fort Belvoir, VA, 1986).

Becker, William H. *From the Atlantic to the Great Lakes. A History of the U.S. Army Corps of Engineers and the St. Lawrence Seaway* (Fort Belvoir, VA, 1984).

Elliott, D. O. *The Improvement of the Lower Mississippi River for Flood Control and Navigation* (3 Volumes, Vicksburg, MS, 1932).

Hays, Samuel P. *Conservation and the Gospel of Efficiency: The Progressive Conservation Movement, 1890–1920* (Cambridge, 1959).

Ferejohn, John A. *Pork Barrel Politics: Rivers and Harbors Legislation, 1947–1968* (Stanford, 1974).

Hill, Forrest G. *Roads, Rails, and Waterways: The Army Engineers and Early Transportation* (Norman, OK, 1957).

Holland, Francis Ross, Jr. *America's Lighthouses: Their Illustrated History Since 1716* (Brattleboro, MA, 1972).

Holmes, Beatrice Hort. *A History of Federal Water Resources Programs, 1800–1960* (Washington, DC, 1972).

Holmes, Beatrice Hort. *History of Federal Water Resources Programs and Policies, 1961–70* (Washington, DC, 1979).

Holt, W. Stull. *The Office of the Chief of Engineers of the Army: Its Nonmilitary History, Activities and Organization* (Baltimore, 1923).

Hoyt, William G., and Walter B. Langbein. *Flocds* (Princeton, 1955).

Humphreys, Andrew A., and Henry L. Abbot. *Report Upon the Physics and Hydraulics of the Mississippi River, Upon the Protection of the Alluvial Region Against Overflow, and Upon the Deepening of the Mouths.* 2d ed. (Washington, DC, 1876).

Johnson, Leland R. "Army Engineers on the Cumberland and Tennessee, 1842–1854." *Tennessee Historical Quarterly* 31 (Summer 1972): 149–69.

Johnson, Leland R. "Waterways: The Fourth Pillar of Defense." *The Military Engineer* 72 (November–December 1980): 404–08.

Lippincott, Isaac. "A History of River Improvement." *Journal of Political Economy* 22 (July 1914): 630–50.

Maass, Arthur. *Muddy Waters: The Army Engineers and the Nation's Rivers* (Cambridge, MA, 1951).

Mazmanian, Daniel A., and Jeanne Nienaber. *Can Organizations Change: Environmental Protection, Citizen Participation and the Corps of Engineers* (Washington, DC, 1979).

Moore, Jamie W., and Dorothy P. Moore. *The Army Corps of Engineers and the Evolution of Federal Flood Plain Management Policy* (Boulder, CO, 1989).

Morgan, Arthur E. *Dams and Other Disasters: A Century of the Army Corps of Engineers in Civil Works* (Boston, 1971).

Nichols, Roger L. "Army Contributions to River Transportation, 1818–1825." *Military Affairs* 33 (April 1959): 242–49.

Power, Garrett. "The Fox in the Chicken Coop: The Regulatory Program of the U.S. Army Corps of Engineers." *Virginia Law Review* 63 (1977): 503–59.

Reuss, Martin. "Andrew A. Humphreys and the Development of Hydraulic Engineering: Politics and Technology in the Army Corps of Engineers, 1850–1950." *Technology and Culture* 26 (January 1985): 1–33.

Reuss, Martin. "The Army Corps of Engineers and Flood-Control Politics on the Lower Mississippi." *Louisiana History* 23 (Spring 1982): 131–48.

Reuss, Martin. "Coping with Uncertainty: Social Scientists, Engineers, and Federal Water Planning," *Natural Resources Journal* 32 (Winter 1992): 101–135.

Reuss, Martin. *Designing the Bayous: The Control of Water in the Atchafalaya Basin, 1800-1995* (Washington, DC, 1998).

Reuss, Martin. "Reshaping National Water Politics: The Emergence of the Water Resources Development Act of 1986." *IWR Policy Study* 91-PS-1 (Fort Belvoir, VA, 1991).

Reuss, Martin. *Shaping Environmental Awareness: The United States Army Corps of Engineers Environmental Advisory Board 1970–1980* (Washington, DC, 1983).

Shallat, Todd A. "Building Waterways, 1802–1861: Science and the United States Army in Early Public Works." *Technology and Culture* 31 (January 1990): 18–50.

Shallat, Todd A. *Structures in the Stream: Water, Science, and the Rise of the U.S. Army Corps of Engineers* (Austin, 1994).

Shallat, Todd A. "Water and Bureaucracy: Origins of the Federal Responsibility for Water Resources, 1787–1838." *Natural Resources Journal* 32 (Winter 1992): 5–25.

Smith, Frank E. *The Politics of Conservation* (New York, 1966).

Stine, Jeffrey K. *Mixing the Waters: Environment, Politics, and the Building of the Tennessee-Tombigbee Waterway* (Akron, OH, 1993).

Stine, Jeffrey K. "The Tennessee-Tombigbee Waterway and the Evolution of Cultural Resources Management." *The Public Historian* 14 (Spring 1992): 6–30.

Sturgis, Samuel D., Jr. "Floods." *The Annals of the American Academy of Political and Social Science* 309 (January 1957): 15–22.

U.S. Army Corps of Engineers. *National Waterways Roundtable Papers: Proceedings on the History and Evolution of U.S. Waterways and Ports* (Fort Belvoir, VA, 1981).

Walker, Paul K. "Building American Canals." *Water Spectrum* 12 (Winter 1979–80): 18–25; (Summer 1980): 12–23.

Wood, Lance D., and John R. Hill, Jr. "Wetlands Protection: The Regulatory Role of the U.S. Army Corps of Engineers." *Coastal Zone Management Journal* 4 (1978): 371–407.

IV. DISASTER RELIEF

Burgess, Carter L. "The Armed Forces in Disaster Relief." *The Annals of the American Academy of Political and Social Science* 309 (January 1957): 71–79.

Cooling, B. Franklin. "The Army and Flood and Disaster Relief." *The United States Army in Peacetime: Essays in Honor of the Bicentennial 1775–1975*. Edited by Robin Higham and Carol Brandt (Manhattan, KS, 1978): 198–200.

Deakyne, Herbert. "Bridging Kaw River in the 1903 Flood." *The Military Engineer* 20 (May–June 1928): 198–200.

Johnson, Leland R. "19th Century Engineering: The Johnstown Disaster." *The Military Engineer* 66 (January–February 1974): 42–45.

McCullough, David G. *The Johnstown Flood* (New York, 1968).

McDonnell, Janet A. *Response to the Loma Prieta Earthquake* (Fort Belvoir, VA, 1993).

McDonnell, Janet A. *The U.S. Army Corps of Engineers Response to the Exxon Valdez Oil Spill* (Fort Belvoir, VA, 1992).

Walker, Paul K. *The Corps Responds: A History of the Susquehanna Engineer District and Tropical Storm Agnes* (Baltimore, 1976).

V. SURVEYS AND EXPLORATIONS

Baldwin, Kenneth H. *Enchanted Enclosure: The Army Engineers and Yellowstone National Park: A Documentary History* (Washington, DC, 1976).

Bartlett, Richard A. *Great Surveys of the American West* (Norman, OK, 1962).

Beers, Henry P. "History of the U.S. Topographical Engineers, 1813–1863." *The Military Engineer* 34 (June 1942): 287–91; (July 1942): 348–52.

Goetzmann, William H. *Army Exploration in the American West 1803–1863* (New Haven, 1959).

Nichols, Roger L., and Patrick L. Halley. *Stephen Long and American Frontier Exploration* (Newark, NJ, 1980).

Schubert, Frank N. *The Nation Builders: A Sesquicentennial History of the Corps of Topographical Engineers, 1838–1863* (Fort Belvoir, VA, 1988).

Schubert, Frank N. *Vanguard of Expansion: Army Engineers in the Trans-Mississippi West 1819–1879* (Washington, DC, 1980).

VI. AUTOBIOGRAPHY AND BIOGRAPHY

Bishop, Joseph B., and Farnham Bishop. *Goethals: Genius of the Panama Canal, A Biography* (New York, 1930).

Clark, Edward B. *William L. Sibert, The Army Engineer* (Philadelphia, 1930).

Dodds, Gordon B. *Hiram Martin Chittenden: His Public Career* (Lexington, 1973).

Franzwa, Gregory M., and William J. Ely. *Leif Sverdrup, Engineer Soldier at His Best* (Gerald, MO, 1980).

Freeman, Douglas S. *R. E. Lee, A Biography* (4 Volumes, New York, 1934–35).

Fremont, John C. *Memoirs of My Life...* (New York, 1887).

Gifford, Emerson. *Gouverneur Kemble Warren: The Life and Letters of an American Soldier, 1830–1882* (Boston, 1932).

Haiman, Miecislaus. *Kosciuszko in the American Revolution* (New York, 1943).

Heusser, Albert H. *George Washington's Map Maker: A Biography of Robert Erskine.* Edited by Hubert G. Schmidt (New Brunswick, NJ, 1966).

Holden, Edward. *Biographical Memoir of William H. C. Bartlett* (Washington, DC, 1911).

Humphreys, Henry H. *Andrew Atkinson Humphreys, A Biography* (Philadelphia, 1924).

Kite, Elizabeth S. *Brigadier-General Louis Lebègue Duportail* (Baltimore, 1933).

McAndrews, Eugene V. "Custer's Engineer —William Ludlow." *The Military Engineer* 61 (May–June 1969): 200–02.

McAndrews, Eugene V. "Sergeant Major Frederick Gerber: Engineer Legend." *The Military Engineer* 63 (July–August 1971): 240–41.

Mumey, Nolie. *John Williams Gunnison (1812–1853): The Last of the Western Explorers* (Denver, 1955).

Myers, William S. *General George Brinton McClellan* (New York, 1934).

Nevins, Allan. *Fremont: Pathmarker of the West* (2 Volumes, New York, 1961).

Nichols, Maj. Gen. K.D., U.S.A. (Ret.). *The Road to Trinity: A Personal*

Account of How America's Nuclear Policies Were Made (New York, 1987).

Smith, Jean Edward. *Lucius D. Clay* (New York, 1990).

Swift, Joseph Gardner. *Memoirs.* Edited by Harrison Ellery (Worcester, MA, 1890).

Talbot, Theodore. *Soldier in the West: Letters of Theodore Talbot During His Service in California, Mexico, and Oregon, 1845–53* (Norman, OK, 1972).

Weigley, Russell F. *Quartermaster General of the Union Army: A Biography of M. C. Meigs* (New York, 1959).

Whaley, Elizabeth M. *Forgotten Hero: General James B. McPherson: The Biography of a Civil War General* (New York, 1955).

Williams, Thomas Harry. *P. G. T. Beauregard: Napoleon in Gray* (Baton Rouge, 1955).

Wilson, James Harrison. *Life and Ser-vices of William Farrar Smith* (Wilmington, DE, 1904).

Wood, Richard G. *Stephen Harriman Long, 1784–1864: Army Engineer, Explorer, Inventor* (Glendale, CA, 1966).

VII. ORAL HISTORY INTERVIEWS

1. Engineer Memoirs

Major General Hugh J. Casey. Interviewed by John T. Greenwood (Washington, DC, 1993).

Lieutenant General Frederick J. Clarke. Interviewed by Albert E. Cowdrey,

Suellen Hoy, and Michael C. Robinson (Washington, DC, 1979).

Lieutenant General Ernest Graves. Interviewed by Frank N. Schubert (Washington, DC, 1997).

General William M. Hoge. Interviewed by Maj. Gen. George Robertson (Washington, DC, 1993).

Frederick McNeely. Interviewed by Frank N. Schubert (Washington, DC, 1987).

Major General William E. Potter. Interviewed by Martin Reuss (Washington, DC, 1983).

Lieutenant General Edward O. Rowny. Interviewed by Barry W. Fowle. (Washington, DC, 1995).

Lieutenant General Arthur G. Trudeau. Interviewed by Col. Calvin J. Landau (Washington, DC, 1986).

Lieutenant General Walter K. Wilson, Jr. Interviewed by Paul K. Walker (Washington, DC, 1984).

2. Engineer Profiles: The District Engineer

Colonel William W. Badger. Interviewed by Frank N. Schubert (Washington, DC, 1983).

3. Water Resources People and Issues

William R. Gianelli. Interviewed by Martin Reuss (Washington, DC, 1985).

Arthur Maass. Interviewed by Martin Reuss (Washington, DC, 1989).

Gilbert F. White. Interviewed by Martin Reuss (Washington, DC, 1993).

Former Seal of the U.S. Army Corps of Engineers
The shield incorporated emblems of the U.S. Army Corps of Engineers (left) and the Corps of Topographic Engineers (right), reunited in 1863.

Unit Crest of the U.S. Army Corps of Engineers

The official unit crest, adopted after the Corps became a Major Army Command in 1979, includes the historic motto, "Essayons" or "Let Us Try."

CPSIA information can be obtained at www.ICGtesting.com
Printed in the USA
BVOW09s0541170116

433159BV00002BB/21/P